C000180207

GRANDDAD'S RAINBOW

First published in 2010 by

WOODFIELD PUBLISHING LTD
Bognor Regis ~ West Sussex ~ England ~ PO21 5EL
www.woodfieldpublishing.co.uk

© Joan Blackburn, 2010

All rights reserved.
No part of this publication may be reproduced
or transmitted in any form or by any means,
electronic or mechanical, nor may it be stored
in any information storage and retrieval system,
without prior permission from the publisher.

The right of Joan Blackburn
to be identified as Author of this work
has been asserted in accordance with
the Copyright, Designs and Patents Act 1988

ISBN 1-84683-093-1

Granddad's Rainbow

Adventures of a War Baby 1939-51

Joan Blackburn
(Neé Ratcliff)

Woodfield

Woodfield Publishing Ltd

Woodfield House ~ Babsham Lane ~ Bognor Regis ~ West Sussex ~ PO21 5EL

telephone 01243 821234 ~ **e-mail** enquiries@woodfieldpublishing.co.uk

Interesting and informative books on a variety of subjects

For full details of all our published titles, visit our website at

www.woodfieldpublishing.co.uk

"They will disappear, those parents who are taking so long to make way for you; they will disappear, those careful watchers over your childhood, those lovely protectors of your adolescence, they will disappear and you will search in vain for better friends. They will disappear and as soon as they are no longer here, they will strike you in a new light because time, which makes older those who are alive, makes them seem younger as soon as death has taken them away...."

Anon

In memory of

Lily and Stan

~ CONTENTS ~

Illustrations

About the Author

Joan Ratcliff was born in Woking, Surrey in 1941 whilst her father, Stan, was serving with the RAF in Malta. After he came home the family moved to live in a converted train carriage at Walton on Thames until re-housed in 1951. Joan joined the WRAF for four years in 1959 and in 1964 she wrote about her experiences in her first book *Naafi Knickers and Nijmegen,* which remained unpublished until 2009.

Joan Blackburn, 2009.

She ran a Girls Venture Corps cadet unit in the 60s and eventually rejoined the WRAF in 1971, where she met and married RAF airman Norman Blackburn.

The couple had two children, Catherine and David, with David following the family tradition and currently serving in the RAF.

Norman and Joan are now retired and live in Littlehampton, West Sussex.

Introduction

This book has been written, for the most part, through the eyes of a child born at the beginning of the forties, when World War II was in its second year. It tells of the love and dedication of a young wife for her RAF husband as she waits for the war that began the week before her wedding day, to end – and normal family life to begin.

Set against the background of the austere forties it also takes a retrospective look at the family history and shows how one split second decision made in one generation can so influence those in the next.

Both informative and sometimes funny, it is a combination of childish innocence, family stories and research. The early dialogue is, of necessity imagined. The people and events, however, are very real – as is their legacy.

In 1939 the World changed for ever – so did the lives of Lily and Stan…

1. *"It will soon be over..."*

1944 – Gardener's Cottage, Coxhill, Chobham

Alice Ratcliff dried the dishes and looked on as her husband held their three-year-old granddaughter in his arms and told her outrageous stories about the images they could both see in the glowing logs and bits of coal on the fire. The man she had married forty years ago was telling yarns about 'fairies' that were disappearing up the chimney amongst the flames. It was so out-of-character in comparison with his usual gruff and down-to-earth demeanour that she had to smother her laughter by burying her face in a tea towel.

He was sixty now but seemed older in many ways. His experiences in the First World War had undoubtedly left their mark. He was 'as tough as old boots' but his granddaughter was certainly not intimidated by that and hung on to his every word as Alice listened to the distant sound of an air raid siren going off somewhere.

"See Joannie!" he pointed. "There – a fairy is on her way up the chimney, and there – see where that piece of coal is? That can be her house."

She peered into the orange and red shapes, safe in the arms of her Granddad.

It was September 1944 and Charles Ratcliff was the only man who was constant in the child's life. He and Granny had been there when she and Mummy had gone away and they had been there when they came back – rocks in an otherwise topsy-turvy world. The man they called her father had drifted in and out of her life at various intervals but she didn't really know him – not yet anyway – and the sound of sirens meant nothing to her.

Lily looked on from a distance, half listening to her father-in-law's ever more fantastic stories and half trying to concentrate on writing to the husband she had seen precious little of in the five years since their wedding day. Like anybody else, all she wanted was a normal life in her own house somewhere and to raise a family. People kept saying that it would soon be over – she almost laughed out loud as she thought of all the people who, in 1939, were saying that it would all be finished by Christmas!

"Huh!" she thought to herself as she checked the bottle of ink to see how much was left in the bottom, *"some hopes!"*

Alice, who, for some inexplicable reason was always called 'Kate' by Charles, put the tea towel away and settled down to her knitting while Lily tried her best to get back to her letter. How many of these had she written since 1939 and how many bottles of ink had she got through?

Five years earlier – September 1939

Of course, nobody had been surprised when the brown envelope marked OHMS came through the letter-box of the Gardener's Cottage on the Coxhill Manor Estate, where Charles was the head gardener. It was calling Stan into the Royal Air Force because of the war that now seemed inevitable, despite Neville Chamberlain waving his bit of paper and saying "peace in our time"! However, it was not as though he did not know what it was all about for he had joined up voluntarily ten years previously, in 1929, when he was just eighteen and the RAF only in its infancy. Then it had been exciting and new – a 'Boy's Own' adventure – as aeroplanes became ever more commonplace and new ones were being designed in rapid succession.

Now though, he had 'done his bit' and was ready to settle down. It had been a wrench to come out and he had missed it but he had settled into his civilian job as a motor mechanic and driver and had also become engaged to Lily. He did not bargain for his plans being wrecked by a war with Germany, which now seemed imminent.

Also imminent was his wedding day, planned for 16th September!

Lily and his mother were already busy making the dress from white parachute silk, whilst his sisters, Rosa and Doris, were sewing the bridesmaids' dresses. The cake was made and the carnations for the wedding bouquet came from the gardens owned by Charles' employers, Mr. and Mrs Christopher Gabriel.

It was of no consequence though. Stan had to report to his unit on 25th August 1939 or be jailed as a deserter. Lily was devastated and Charles and Alice felt as though history was repeating itself.

However, it still wasn't actual war – yet – and it wasn't as though he had to go and do square-bashing all over again. There were a few perks to having been in the RAF before – he had ten years' experience in his chosen trade and would get rapid promotion and therefore likely to be an NCO in no time, giving him status and extra money. Not only that, he did know a bit about what to expect – unlike his poor father, a generation before, who did not have a clue what he was going into.

Lily, on the other hand, was not in the least bit impressed, nor as optimistic.

Within days of receiving his papers Stan was kitted out and before August turned to September he was sent off to Plymouth to help in the evacuation of the people from the Channel Islands. Lily received a letter from him assuring her that he would get some leave to get married on the planned date and maybe war would not be declared after all,

"Perhaps it is still a 'phony war'" he wrote, *"you never know, things may all die down and I'll be home in no time."*

It was a vain hope. On 1st September 1939, Hitler invaded Poland and everything changed for everybody. Two days later Neville Chamberlain announced to the Nation that we "were now at war with Germany." All leave was cancelled from that moment and children were evacuated to the countryside in their droves. Then, as if that wasn't enough, Lily received a letter from Stan to say that he was to be posted to France just 48 hours after their proposed wedding day. She couldn't believe it – it was as if the 'world and his wife' were dead set against their proposed nuptials. France might as well have been Australia as far as she was concerned.

"Don't worry" he wrote, *"I will grovel on my hands and knees to the C.O. if necessary – we'll get married no matter what."*

As it turned out, a very understanding Commanding Officer granted him permission to have one weekend off for his wedding on the 16th – but he had to be back at camp on the 18th September ready for his deployment to France. Little did Lily know it then, but it would be a year before she would see him again . The only consolation was that there were thousands of people in the same situation and everybody was just as scared as everybody else.

Then, to add 'insult to the injury', in her eyes anyway, on arrival at Lille in Northern France they billeted Stan with a middle-aged widow and her two teenage daughters, Genevieve and Jacqueline! In truth she was quite jealous of the girls but she tried not to show it – after all it **was** wartime and it would all be over in five minutes – or so they were constantly being told. However, she could not begin to know how much danger her new husband and his hosts were in, never mind the further risks they would take just one year later, and it was just as well!

Summer 1940 – Occupied France

In fact, Lille was constantly under siege with the French and British trying to push back the advancing German Army.

By May the allies were in retreat from the border and, despite the best efforts of the Resistance, Northern France was invaded by Germany and our own troops were ordered to make for Dunkirk, from where the biggest evacuation ever staged would take place. It was called Operation Dynamo.

The girls, whose colouring was an advert to their Jewish ancestry, and who, after all, were 'aiding the enemy of the Germans' realised how vulnerable they were going to be with the British retreating and so, like thousands of others, they decided it would be best to head south.

The allies were losing badly and the position of the girls and their mother was a real worry to Stan. Although neither spoke the other's language they had looked after him and fed him and made him comfortable through, at times, enormous hardship to themselves and with the fighting going on all around them. He couldn't leave them to their fate. In his eyes he had no choice.

Stan with Genevieve and Jacqueline.

He hid all three of them in the back of his RAF vehicle and drove them south to relatives who lived on the outskirts of Paris instead of taking the forty-mile trip north-west to Dunkirk. Over 300,000 troops were rescued from the beaches and Churchill called it a 'miracle of deliverance.' However over 5,000 soldiers were killed in the evacuation and the RAF lost 474 planes. Meanwhile Stan risked being captured by the enemy in his bid to get the girls to comparative safety amid the chaos.

At the time it was unthinkable that Hitler would get as far as Paris and Stan could hardly believe it when on the 10th June Italy sided with Germany. By the 14th June "Adolf was strutting around the capital city of France like a turkey cock".

In the meantime, and using up some of his 'nine lives' Stan finally made it to the French coast and was picked up by a ship to cross the Channel. He managed to make it back to Uxbridge unaware of the fate of the girls and their mother. He had certainly saved their lives getting them out of Lille, but whether it was 'from the frying pan into the fire' he had no way of knowing.

As to Lily, she was none the wiser. Like his father before him, the nearer he came to 'losing his nine lives' as he put it, the less he wanted to talk about it.

Summer 1940 – Hyde Cottage, Woking,

Whilst Stan was in France, Lily, blissfully unaware of the narrow escapes he was having, lived with her parents in their primitive old cottage and got herself a job in Sainsbury's. At least she had the company of the other girls to take her mind off things and she tried to write to Stan every day never knowing if the mail would reach him or not or how much would be crossed out by the censor.

Life in the cramped surroundings of the old fashioned homestead that she had been brought up in until she was fourteen was not very successful though. Her younger brothers and sisters were still at home and there was simply not enough room for her as well. They did not have proper plumbing and, she was realising that, what she took to be normal as a child, was actually very old fashioned indeed. She was the eldest of eight and had been sent away into service at the age of fourteen in order to *make* room for the younger ones – they did not expect her to come back again!

She wished with all her heart that her father would get himself into the twentieth century!

"Oh, he is a selfish old bugger!" she would say to her mother every time she came back from a visit to the tin toilet in the back of the house and had washed it liberally with Jeyes Fluid.

When Stan finally came home from France, escaping the carnage of Dunkirk, she was only too glad to move in with him and his parents. He was only home for a few days before reporting back to Uxbridge at the height of the Battle of Britain If they thought that they would see much of each other during that summer and autumn of 1940 they were to be disappointed. His time in the U.K. coincided with some of the worst battles of the war in the skies over London. The RAF were fighting for our very survival in the air and there was very little in the way of leave or passes for anyone.

Everyone had said that it would all be over after the Battle of Britain, but nobody believed anything any more, unless of course it came from the lips of Churchill. Lily, like everyone else, heard his stirring words after the RAF had fended off the enemy that summer.

"Never in the field of human conflict had so much been owed by so many to so few!" he had said, and it didn't take long for people to realise how right he had been. However, those who thought that the end was in sight were wrong. It certainly was not – it had barely started.

When Lily found herself to be pregnant she moved permanently into the Gardener's Cottage with her husband's family.

2. *"God is on our side – isn't he?"*

1944 – Gardener's Cottage

Lily brought her thoughts back to 1944. It was no good – she couldn't concentrate on letter writing with all the squeals coming from over by the fireplace every time her daughter thought she saw a fairy!

"Five more minutes young lady and then it is your bed time," she chided. "Honestly Dad, how on earth can I concentrate on writing to Stan?

It was a lost cause. She put her pen down, put the top on the ink bottle and gave up. He would be going off to his Home Guard unit in a little while and then they would all get some peace!

"Still," she thought to herself, "If Stan had not been so keen on looking after those French girls he may have been killed at Dunkirk and this child wouldn't be here anyway." It was a sobering thought!

Joan listened to her Granddad's stories sweetly oblivious to the turmoil that everyone was in. Mummy kept telling her who the handsome man in the photograph by her bed was and that he was away in the war. They said he was in the RAF too but she didn't know what that meant and so the 'fireside stories' about fairies with her Granddad represented routine and safety in her life.

Even at her young age she could remember being taken away from her grandparents and she did not like it one bit.

Everyone was thoroughly fed up with it all, and sometimes very scared, but she was only vaguely aware of the anxious rush to the door when the postman arrived or the complete silence when the News was on the wireless. Already she knew she had to be quiet when people were listening to the latest events because they could have something to do with the man in the photographs.

"Look, there's another fairy," said Charles, "look there – she is going up the chimney and she is going to burn the bottoms of all those bloomin' starlings that are on my roof."

"Charles!" cried Alice. She was trying to count the stitches on her knitting needle but it was impossible. He was doing it on purpose now!

Lily put her writing pad away until later and let her mind drift back to before the child was born. Stan had always written letters too, but never more so than when he went to Malta with the Second Expeditionary Force so soon after she became pregnant...

Autumn 1940 – Malta

Having already spent a year in France Stan thought that he just might get a few months at home in the U.K. but no such luck – in no time at all he got his posting to Malta and by November he was on board HMS Newcastle waiting for orders to set sail.

He started writing home even before he left Uxbridge. He wrote one from the barracks and posted it there and then, and he wrote another letter while he sat and waited with all the other men on the quayside at Plymouth. He also wrote again the next day as everyone sat in the hold waiting for the orders to move out of harbour.

The boredom was the worst part as for six more days the ship stayed put and he wrote even more letters and started to keep a diary.

"This time would have been better spent on leave" he wrote angrily.

It took six more days to get to Malta and there he was to remain for the next two and a half years.

The tiny island, which was so strategically important to both Allies and Germans alike, was under constant bombardment from the Luftwaffe and from the Italian Air Force and shipping. Only a regular supply of letters from home and the news that he was to become a father kept Stan's morale up. He tried his best to make as light as possible of a deadly situation.

"Two dive bomb attacks today," he wrote, *"if it is not the Jerry it is the blessed eye-tyes – we claim 13 brought down though home radio says 23 – wish it was 103!"*

1940/41 – Gardener's Cottage

Back home, Lily soldiered on through the winter of 1940 and the spring of 1941. France had been bad enough. Charles had been absolutely 'beside himself' when the Italians joined in on Germany's side back in June.

"Bloody turncoats!" he exclaimed. "Just shows you not to trust bloody eye-tyes – the war would have been won by now if it wasn't for them."

. The reports on the wireless about the battering that Malta was getting, from air and sea, did nothing to help anyone's sanity and then, in June, the baby girl was born.

She was helped into the world, by Miss Enid – Mr. and Mrs. Gabriel's daughter. She was assisting in the maternity hospital as part of her war work and she cycled all the way home on her bike in order to be the first to tell Charles the momentous news! He was in the big greenhouse at the back of Coxhill Manor at the time.

"Ratcliff, Ratcliff!" she cried, as she pushed her bike across the vegetable gardens towards him. "You have a healthy granddaughter."

"Oh thank you Miss Enid."

He touched the brim of his trilby hat in the time honoured way and then strode off across the nearby field to tell Alice. It was great to have some good news for a change.

As soon as Lily arrived back from the maternity hospital all Charles wanted to do was to send his son a picture of the child. However that wasn't straightforward either! Letters to Malta were censored and it was almost impossible to send a photograph. Almost – but not quite. Charles was not to be beaten by 'damn censors' as he called them and he had a very good 'box Brownie' camera!

He took a photo of the week old baby as she lay in her pram. Once it was developed he carefully cut out her head and stuck it under the stamp of a letter that he wrote himself to his son.

"There you are Lil'" he cried triumphantly, "at least the boy can see a picture of the child now – it will take more than a damn censor to beat me!"

"How will he know where to look?" said Lily.

"The boy is not daft Lil'" he answered. "It's always you or his mother that does the writing – one from me and he will study it very carefully indeed."

1941 – Malta

Unbeknown to everyone at home, on the very day that his child was born Stan, still unaware that he had become a father, was put on Guard Duty all night.

He wasn't very happy about it because it wasn't his turn and it was a job usually left to junior ranks anyway. However, as it turned out he had reason to be very grateful.

He watched, almost in fascination, at the dog fights between Italians and the RAF going on above him and the sight of Valletta Harbour all lit up with bombs and incendiaries and fire from the ships.

Then, suddenly, with no warning, the camp became the main target and, to his horror, from his vantage point on 'look out' he could only stare helpless as his billet received a direct hit. All the blokes who he had been laughing and joking with just a few hours before were killed outright.

"Had a narrow escape from bomb on M7," he wrote in his diary afterwards, *"Fierce night raid on island. Three brought down though."*

A few days later the letter from his father arrived. Like the old man had said 'he was not daft' and it didn't take him long to find the photo. For some time it was the only record he had of the birth of his daughter – one tiny picture a little more than a quarter of an inch square.

Two Christmas's came and went and Stan continued to keep his diary up to date while, back home, all everyone could do was count the weeks and then the months and then the years...

Stan, wearing hat, with blokes from M7.

The billet after a direct hit.

"25th Christmas Day" he wrote, *"(wet) Nothing doing in the way of flying. Quite nice dinner but what a noise. You have to fight for anything here. Most of them drunk. The Governor came round after dinner and spoke a few words but still with plenty of row and racing around.*

I would swap it all for one minute at home right now. I expect they are quiet at home. Probably Lil is with them too. Well let's hope we will all be together again next year."

The two and a half years of bombing, little time off and lack of decent food took its toll and Stan eventually contracted sand fly fever. He was admitted to the 90th General Hospital at Imtarfa in Malta. However, even this place was a prime target for the enemy bombers and received constant battering. There was no let up in the German and Italian efforts to bring Malta to its knees. If Stan had nine lives he felt he must have used them all up by now.

Finally he was invalided back home to a British RAF Hospital where he stayed until he was fully recovered. But that still wasn't the end of it – oh no, not by a long chalk...

1944 – Gardener's Cottage

Lily's thoughts were interrupted once again by the excited cries of the three year old.

"Oh look Granddad – more fairies in the fire, see that one?" Joan squealed.

"I missed it!" replied Charles as he continued to poke the embers, "I bet she has gone way up across the skies and she is going to find your father and bring him home safely for ever."

"And we will never have to go away on that big train again?!" she said suddenly.

Charles was mildly surprised that she still remembered though it was only last year.

"I hope not" he replied, and then changed the subject rapidly because he knew that she might very well have to. It wasn't all over yet and so far they had been lucky that she was too young to be evacuated without her mother. He grimaced at the thought of her being sent off with a label attached to her coat like so many in the years previously.

"There's another fairy there!" he continued, "look, down there" he moved the dying embers around with the brass handled poker and more sparks flew up. "See Joannie, between the big dark mountains, and soon the naughty fairy will *chase* her away!"

On the word 'chase' he put the poker down and tickled her tummy before lifting her to the floor and glancing across at the clock.

"Right – that's enough Dad!" said Lily to the man who treated her like one of his own daughters, "The five minutes is up – It's time that Joan got ready for bed."

Only Lily ever called her child by the name she was christened with and steadfastly stuck to it against overwhelming odds. Alice put down her knitting and placed the saucepan on the stove to warm some milk.

"That's the end of the stories for today," she smiled, "time for supper my dear – Granddad has to go out soon to do his duty – and"... she scowled in the direction of the culprit by the fire, "if Granddad carries on using up our bits of coal and firewood we will all go cold!"

"Oh get away with you woman," he grunted. "I'll go and get some more logs off the common." He put the big heavy guard around the fire though and ended the stories – he did have to go and do his duty.

Charles Ratcliff was a stocky man but without an ounce of excess flesh on his body, and his skin was weathered and brown from a lifetime spent in the outdoors. What was left of his hair, which was very little, was white and in wisps on either side of his bald head and he had a small dent in the top. This was a reminder, as if one were needed, of how close some of the shrapnel came to killing him when he was on the Somme nearly thirty years previously.

He had a little 'toothbrush style' white moustache covering his upper lip and the kindest of pale blue eyes which totally gave away the gentleness beneath his gruff exterior.

Alice poured the warm milk onto some broken up pieces of bread and Lily put two big cushions on the chair at the table and lifted her daughter up onto them. This plain supper was all there was in this time of austerity. The rationing was as acute as it had ever been but the child didn't know any different or missed what she had never had.

"Eat right down until you can see the bottom of the bowl," said the old lady, "It will make your bones strong."

She caught sight of herself in the mirror above the fireplace. She was five years older than Charles and felt it lately.

"Goodness" she said out loud to nobody in particular, "It's my mother looking back at me!"

Actually, she had always been very beautiful and still had a mop of black hair, with hardly a hint of grey, and dark brown eyes. Her fashion never varied though. Like everyone, she had to 'make do and mend' so all her dresses were of the same style and material and she still favoured the fashion that she was used to – dating back to the turn of the century with a skirt that almost touched the ankles. All attempts by her daughters, Rosa and the younger Doris, to get her 'up-to-date' were lost on her.

"No, I'll leave the shorter skirts to you girls," she would laugh. "In my day a young man preferred a well turned ankle to bony knees."

She was born in Stanley Road, East Sheen in 1879 and had seen many changes since then. She had started her working life at the age of fourteen in service for the gentry beginning 'below stairs', but by 1907 she had progressed to 'above stairs', becoming a parlour maid at the prestigious house of Lord Downshire at Easthampstead in Berkshire.

It was at this grand house that she met and fell in love with Charles Ratcliff, the 'unrefined and down-to-earth' young gardener who had just moved south from his home in Northamptonshire to look for work. From the minute he set eyes on her he called her 'Kate' but she patiently endured it, and eventually even her parents found themselves getting used to his cheek which seemed to include changing their daughter's name!

Unlike Alice's ancestors, who were 'townies', all his forebears had been gardeners or agricultural labourers – 'turnip tops' he affectionately called them – the 'salt of the earth'

The couple married in 1908 and were happy and contented, living in the tied cottage on the estate. They later moved to East Sussex where their three children, Rosa,

Stanley and Doris were born. Then everyone's lives changed with the outbreak of the First World War.

Very few families escaped losses and Alice was shattered when her younger brother, Charlie, was killed – the fact that he had been awarded the DCM was little consolation to her, or her parents, and she certainly did not expect that a generation later she would see her only son involved in yet another World War. The last one was supposed to have been the 'one to end them all' and it was also supposed to never happen again. It had been too awful for words.

She tried to stop her mind wandering and forced her thoughts back to happier times as she cleared away her granddaughter's clean bowl – like the time when Charles came home after recovering from his injuries and the relief she had felt to see him again after nearly four years away.

Then, with the Great War finally over, the family moved to the peaceful village of Chobham where Charles took up the post of head gardener for Mr. Gabriel. From that moment on they put the events of 1914-18 behind them – it was something that they just did not talk about – especially Charles. He did not want to relive it by discussing it with anyone.

Alice gave herself a little mental shake. It was already getting quite dark and it was time to go round and pull the blackout curtains together. She just hoped that all these people who kept saying 'it will soon be over' were right!

Lily wiped her daughter's face with a flannel and a bit of spit.

"Whatever will your father think of you if he comes home and sees you all mucky!" she said, "you never know, he might come home today."

Alice thought that this could be a bit of 'wishful thinking' but she didn't say so. She was just grateful that Stanley was back from Malta now and not being bombed 'to kingdom come' though, it did seem that nobody was safe anywhere any more.

Charles looked across at his grandchild as Lily brushed her hair and wondered what sort of future she would have to look forward to if Hitler *did* win, and then he immediately put it out of his mind again. He was *not* going to win. He was *not!* There was no chance – you only had to listen to the News – and God is on our side – isn't he?

One of the things that both he and Alice had in common was their total and unflinching belief in the Bible and God. Not only were Charles' parents members of the Salvation Army but Alice's father was a Methodist lay-preacher. They lived their lives by the Ten Commandments and the two wars had not diminished their faith, despite Charles' extremely unchristian thoughts regarding Hitler and Mussolini and what he would like to do to the both of them!

He got up out of his chair and stretched his arms and back.

"Well, I suppose I had better go and do my duty Kate!" he said to Alice and was across the 'kitchen cum living room' in a couple of strides. "I have to go and look for spies again Joannie!"

He put on his Home Guard jacket and took his tin hat from the peg where it had been hanging in the passage. He gave Alice a quick kiss on the cheek.

"Honestly – I did not think he would still be 'doing his duty' now in 1944" she said to Lily, "I reckon he did enough of that in the last lot!"

Joan wasn't quite sure what 'doing his duty' meant, nor what he was looking for pies for. Granny made perfectly good pies with pastry on the big wooden kitchen table where she had just finished eating her bread and milk! All she *did* know was that two or three times each week he put the tin hat on and went on his bike into the village. He always told her the hat was to keep his bald head from getting wet in the rain, and that it was called a 'Guzzunder'.

"Do you know why it is called a Guzzunder Joannie?" he said every time.

She knew the answer to that one by now! Everybody knew the answer to *that* one!

"Because it guzzunder the bed Granddad."

"That's right, aren't you clever?!" The routine never varied! He came over and gave the child a kiss on the top of her head.

"You look after your mother and grandmother" he smiled "and I'll see you in the morning, bright and early with the lark." Joan hoped that he would find his pies all right!

He gave Lily a hand to empty the bathtub of soapy water, which had just been used to get the grime of the day from her offspring, out onto the back garden and then straddled his bike just as the soft groan of aircraft could be heard overhead.

"Well at least they sound like ours," he grunted. He shook his fist to the unseen aeroplanes high up in the darkening sky.

"Go on – give them what for boys – give them what for!"

Lily watched his figure disappear into the gloom and laughed at his final retort as he went round the corner in the blackout.

"If I end up head first in the bloody ditch blame bloody Adolf – I can't see a damn thing."

She loved him dearly and how her life had changed since she had first met his son. She dragged her cardigan further around her shoulders and giggled to herself as Charles cycled out of sight and then shuddered as she remembered her days as a scullery maid.

At the very time her future husband was joining the RAF back in 1929 – just two days after his eighteenth birthday, fourteen year old Lily had been sent into service. She shuddered again at the thought of it – it was just awful.

If Alice had been 'above stairs', she had been *so* 'below stairs' that if she had gone any further down she would have been in the cellar! She would never forget her first day and the sight of heaps of greasy dishes she had to wash. She had, at the time, hated her father for sending her away and felt that she could never forgive him. True, as she got older she progressed from scullery to kitchen maid but it was a very hard life and she only ever got to go home once a month. Her younger brothers and sisters almost forgot she existed. She hated it and ran away on more than one occasion, only to be marched straight back with 'a flee in her ear'.

Then, after eight long, seemingly, never-ending years of drudgery she made friends with the new assistant cook Doris

Ratcliff. Her life changed for ever when the bubbly and sympathetic youngest daughter of the Head Gardener of Coxhill Manor decided to do a bit of 'match-making'. Her circumstances were very different from Lily's in that she was there to learn to be a cook and she went home to her family on most days. Lily smiled to herself as she remembered the laughs she had with her new friend. She had never dreamed that one day she would become her sister-in-law.

Doris was already courting the young chauffeur called Harry and she thought that it was time Lily had a boyfriend too. Then, on one, never to be forgotten day in 1938, she arrived at work full of excitement because her older brother, who she adored, had completed his time in the RAF and was home, they all thought, for good.

Lily felt her heart flutter all over again when she remembered visiting the little bungalow with Doris for the first time and being introduced to Charles and Alice and her brother Stanley– the phrase 'tall, dark and handsome' had never been put to better use!

The sound of Alice singing stopped her thoughts in their tracks and reminded her that she *did* have a daughter to get ready for bed and she hadn't finished her blinkin' letter yet! There was no time for any more trips down 'Memory Lane'.

Her mother-in-law was teaching Joan how to play 'cats-cradle' with a piece of wool when she went back indoors.

"Come on you." demanded Lily as she came back into the 'real world', "Bed!"

Joan kissed her Granny goodnight. She smelt of lavender.

"Goodnight Joannie!" said Alice, "Don't forget your prayers will you dear?"

The young child ran down the passage to the bedroom and knelt on the floor at the side of the big bed, with her hands together, closely watched by Lily in case she missed anyone out.

"God bless Granddad, and Granny, and mummy and my aunties and my other Granny and Granddad, but most of all God bless daddy and bring him home soon" she chanted.

Her eyes were tightly shut so she was unable to see her mother's glum face as she listened to the prayers. Prayers that had been said every single day since the child could speak.

"How much longer was it going to go on for?" thought Lily "five years nearly – five damn years!"

Then she fought back her annoyance and stifled a giggle as the child continued praying…

"…and please help my Granddad to find his pies. Amen"

Lily didn't know whether to laugh out loud or cry as she tucked the three year old into bed. Her fifth wedding anniversary had been and gone, but she could count on one hand the number of days she and Stan had seen each other – as for Christmas, they had never had one together yet. She was convinced that it was only her in-laws that were stopping her from going insane.

She looked across the room at the result of Stan's brief return from France snuggling down into the big bed and counted her blessings once more. Then she went and curled up in the chair by the window and thought about the 'roller-coaster ride' it had been since they were married.

Had she fully known the dangers he had faced in France and then, to crown it all, Malta, never mind the length of time he would be away, she felt that she would be completely grey by now. It would be decades before the full horrors of this war became, even partially, known to her – or anybody else for that matter.

She sat back in the chair by the window – she just wanted to be quiet with her own thoughts.

3. *"After the past five years the next fifty will be a cakewalk..."*

1944 – Gardener's Cottage

Like Charles, Lily was mildly surprised that her daughter had remembered going on the train, but then there *had* been a couple of memorable attempts to accompany her husband when he had returned from Malta and recovered from his illness – though it was unlikely that the child would have recalled the first time.

She giggled quietly as she thought of the look of shocked horror on Charles' face when she announced she was going with Stan on his next posting after he came out of hospital!

He had been sent to RAF Eastchurch on the Isle of Sheppey and this time Lily had been determined that she was going with him. Everyone had tried to put her off. It was even more dangerous there than it was at Chobham and she had a baby to consider

"It's the first place the damn Germans will land!" Charles had exclaimed when he heard her plan – you'll be safer here!"

"Dad, I have seen him once in three and a half years," responded Lily defiantly.

"You can't blame the girl" said Alice as she remembered the similar amount of time that she had waited for Charles in the first lot. She knew she would have done the same.

He had been right though – she winced in the gathering gloom and pulled the blackout curtains tightly shut as she thought back to that trip just last year...

Seeing how determined she was. Stan's cousins, who lived at Sheerness, offered to put her up but she should have paid attention to her father-in-law. He listened avidly to the news on the wireless and always knew best. It could be very annoying!

For a start, she had felt dreadful eating their food. Although she took her ration book, people were genuinely hungry – in fact they still were. Britain was just as much under siege as Malta was. All the beaches were land mined and the rolls of barbed wire everywhere were an awesome sight. Perhaps, if she had been on her own she would have stuck it out but, as everyone kept reminding her, including Stan, there was a baby to consider. They were on the direct flight path of the Luftwaffe coming across the Channel to London and within easy range of the doodlebugs. She seemed to spend every waking moment down the air raid shelter. On top of it all she hardly saw her husband at all as he was continuously on duty. In the end she came back home – for the time being at any rate…

The sound of Alice in the kitchen singing "Count your Blessings" brought her back to the present day again and she suddenly felt extremely guilty at being so miserable. She stood up and carefully rubbed her sleeve over the photo that Joan had left lying on the side table. It had been hastily taken between Stan's postings and the child always kissed it goodnight though she really hadn't a clue who he was.

Lily gave a wry smile to herself as she recalled the occasion when *that* photograph had been taken. It had been taken during a brief moment together at Sheerness when Joan was only two. She could barely remember it being taken now. She hadn't known who her father was from Adam! Consequently, she *would* not stand right in the centre between the two of them no matter what tricks the poor photographer tried.

She was glad they had persevered though because it was the only photo she had of the three of them together and would be the first thing she would grab if there was a fire! Lily took a final look at the infant, who was already asleep, and crept quietly out of the room. She would not hear from her again until morning.

She walked down the passage, vaguely wondering what had become of the French girls that Stan had saved, and almost bumped into his eldest sister Rosa as she came in through the back door! She had been to Red Cross and was still wearing her uniform.

"There is talk down at the Village Hall that it will all soon be over!" said Rosa kindly, "maybe we won't have to wait much longer,"

Spring 1943.

"How long have they been saying that?" replied Lily, "I have heard it so many times before Rosa – it was supposed to be all over in 1940 – even our photo is out of date – I'm the only one she recognises!

"Well at least it shows you've not altered!" she said. "Don't worry Lil', they say the Allies have got right into Europe now – they only need to turf the Germans out of Paris and then it will be the over for good and all!"

"And a good job too!" said Lily.

Rosa was just a little older than Stan – 33 now and, so far, had not found any boyfriend to interest her.

"All the decent ones are overseas fighting the war!" she would say.

"Come on Rosa dear!" said Alice, "I'll get you a cup of tea while you get out of that uniform – you look as though you have earned it this evening!"

"Yes, let's have a little bit of peace before dad comes home," she replied.

"My daughter thinks he is out looking for pies," laughed Lily.

"Bless the child" giggled Alice.

"I wouldn't give a spy much chance if he did find one," said Rosa as she came back into the room minus her apron and a jumper over her dress.

Alice switched the wireless on and the three women settled down for the evening with their sewing or knitting. They were all self-sufficient in that regard, making all their own dresses and even coats.

There was no choice but to 'make do and mend' as clothing coupons only stretched to the equivalent of one outfit per year. Everybody kept a 'rag-bag' where they kept remnants or anything that no longer fitted but which could be used for something else.

Lily had just finished sewing a pair of dungarees for Joan to play in out of the legs of a pair of Charles's old gardening trousers. They had been scrubbed and now were a faded dingy grey and had certainly seen better days. However, she had sewn bright red buttons from an old dress of hers on the pockets and embroidered a red 'J' on the bib.

"There!" she giggled, holding them up in front of her "who said dad's old trousers would not come in handy?!"

Charles was often in the habit of plonking his granddaughter in his wheelbarrow without taking too much notice of what had been in it before her, so these would be ideal.

"He can do his worst!" laughed Alice as they settled down for what was left of the evening.

"I expect he will be home in a minute" said Rosa unnecessarily as she glanced at the clock, "and then our peace will be shattered!"

"I wonder if he has got any pies?" laughed Alice.

Sure enough, a few minutes later and there was the familiar sound of his bike clunking against the wall of the bungalow and the click of the latch as he opened the door. His face was covered in green and black camouflage paint and he had grass sticking out all over him. He was not happy!

"Look at me!" he roared. "Sixty years old and I am crawling around Chobham Common like a twenty year old, and for what? Just to let other sixty year old men pretend to shoot me."

"Well at least they are not Germans Dad!" replied Lily, "they wouldn't be pretending so much then."

"And they are not pies either," giggled Rosa.

"Huh!" grunted Charles, ignoring her. "Oh God Almighty – how I hate Hitler – I wouldn't pretend if I came face to face with him or any of his damned cronies!"

Under different circumstances Lily would have felt sorry for any spy or invader that was unfortunate enough to come into contact with *her* father-in-law! He would take no prisoners and could be quite impressive when angry.

The girls couldn't help but smile kindly at the state of him, but he, like the rest of the old men of the Home Guard took their role very seriously indeed although many of them didn't even have bullets for their guns. They fought for their country before in 'the first lot' and would do it again – hand to hand to the death if need be. They were the 'last resort' if Hitler did get on to mainland Britain.

Alice was already pouring some warm water into the sink for him and Rosa had put away her sewing and was making his cocoa. Lily went and found his slippers.

"Damn good job the Americans came into the war!" he grunted. " Two years too bloody late as ever!"

"Language Charles!" she smiled as she pulled pieces of grass and twigs out of his tin hat while he finished washing his face.

He slumped into his chair and turned up the wireless as the ten o'clock news came on and everyone went quiet.

"*....the allies are poised to enter Paris*" the Newsreader was saying, almost as if he had heard Rosa. Charles silently punched the air in victory!

"That's what I want to hear Kate!" he said to Alice.

"The Germans are on the run....the allied invasion of Normandy earlier in the year was the beginning of the end..."

"There you are Lily!" said Rosa as she put her sewing away, "I told you so."

"*London is being bombarded again by doodlebugs*!" the newsreader went on to say. It was certainly not all good news.

"The V2's with their one ton bombs are replacing the less accurate V1's! – the Government are advising those people with children to evacuate to the West Country out of the reach of these deadly weapons."

They sat in silence and listened to the rest of the News.

London had, of course, already received a pasting from the V1's. At first they had gone all over the place – they had failed to hit their targets and most had fizzled into the sea. The Londoners called them 'Bob Hopes' because all you could do was 'bob down and hope!'. Now here was a second blitz and the V2's had no nickname because they were too dreadful for one! The enemy were desperate and pulling out all the stops in their efforts to beat us..

"Damn Germans!" Charles exclaimed again. He poured his cocoa from his cup into his saucer and blew on it.

All three women exchanged glances and Alice raised her eyes to the heavens. She still hadn't taught him etiquette.

He pretended not to notice.

Lily put away her sewing basket and leant over to give her mother and father-in-law a kiss goodnight, closely followed by Rosa.

"Goodnight everyone and sweet dreams!"

"Sweet dreams dear!" said Alice "sleep well!"

"It really will all be over soon!" said Charles to his daughter-in-law, "I promise!"

He said it as if he, personally, was going to sort Hitler out himself! And he would have done – given half the chance!

"There's one thing Lil'!" said Charles, "If you and Stan are still together after the past five years, then the next fifty will be a cakewalk!"

Lily and Rosa walked down the passage together giggling like schoolgirls as they went.

"Why does your dad call your mother Kate?" whispered Lily as they were about to part company to go to their respective bedrooms.

"Do you know Lil" smiled Rosa, "I honestly do not know – he always has – I didn't know she was called Alice myself until I was quite grown up."

"Haven't you ever asked him?"

"I keep forgetting – anyway I think mum named Stanley after the *road* she was born in, so who knows?"

"And there was I thinking it was after the Stanley who found Livingstone in Africa" giggled Lily, "Anyway *one* day I will find out why he calls her Kate – you see if I don't."

Rosa smiled and went into the room which she once shared with her sister Doris.

There had also been another sister, always referred to as 'young Edie'. Edith Joan had been born late in the lives of Charles and Alice, after he had returned from the Somme. She had been a 'mongol baby'. The description of such a child was eventually changed to 'down's syndrome' but mongol was perfectly acceptable at this time.

She died of pneumonia at the age of just thirteen. That had been twelve or more years ago, but she had never been forgotten and, already Joan knew who 'young Edie' was and that she had been 'a very poorly baby' and she was named after her.

What people called the condition made no difference to the amount that she was loved by the family. As Alice always said "a rose by any other name would still smell as sweet!"

It suddenly occurred to Lily that it might be Charles's philosophy too. Kate or Alice – she was just as sweet!

She went into the bedroom and washed her face and cleaned her teeth in the dark trying not to wake her daughter. In the distance she could hear the rumbling of aircraft engines and the occasional wail of a siren. She went over to the window and peaked out at a watery moon before closing the curtains even tighter together. Then she crawled into bed at the side of her sleeping child and lay awake thinking about her last and final effort at trying to follow Stan! It had been a disaster!

Autumn 1943 – Newcastle

After a few months at Eastchurch, Stan was posted to RAF Usworth near Newcastle. The idea of going all that way did not put Lily off. As her father-in-law had said 'if they could get through this the rest would be a cake-walk'.

"Newcastle!" Charles had exclaimed "They are bombing Newcastle nearly as much as London!" To him it was almost as daft as her going to Sheerness. .

Just for once he was not quite right though. Places that had once been considered as target areas for German bombs, such as Newcastle and Gateshead, were now, strangely, less of a threat than the very vulnerable south-east and over 2,000 mothers and children were eventually evacuated north – out of range of the even deadlier V2's. Nearly 800 families played host to both civilians and service people alike. Also, It had not gone over Lily's head that Stan's ship to Malta had been called 'The Newcastle'. Perhaps it was an 'omen'!

She was determined and when Lily was determined, nothing would shake her. Maybe things would work out better in Newcastle than they did when she had tried to join him at Sheerness. Once again, it had been 'wishful thinking'.

The journey up North had taken hours and the trains were all over the place and heaving with soldiers, sailors and airmen either coming home from 'the front' or going off to join their units or squadrons.

Most of the time the people were a cheery lot, even during the hazardous trip down the corridor taking one or other of their children to the toilet!

However, Lily considered herself very fortunate to have Stan with her as most of the women were travelling alone but she knew this bonus would be very short lived – after all he was on his way to his new unit and, as usual, all leave was cancelled.

She made friends with another 'RAF wife' called Gladys. The continuous sound of the train chugging over the sleepers kept the children dozing off although Joan was unusually grizzly and attention seeking. Stan put it down to the journey but his efforts to pacify her amounted to nothing as he was still a complete stranger to her. Tired and exhausted they were glad to get on the RAF bus that was waiting for them at the station, and after a short drive they arrived at their destination on the outskirts of the city.

"Can anybody hate Hitler as much as I do?" said Gladys as she struggled off the bus with her case and hitched her baby over one shoulder.

Stan could think of plenty – headed by himself, not to mention his dad, who would pay good money to 'pull the rope on him'!

He followed on behind and helped the women and children but Lily knew that he would not be able to stay. He had to report to his new station immediately. He kissed her goodbye and was gone, in an instant, on the same transport that had just dropped them off.

They were soon greeted by the owner of the property, a Mrs. Adams, a tubby middle-aged Geordie woman. Nobody could understand what she was saying but she seemed friendly enough.

However, Lily thought she would pass out when she saw the tiny room at the top of the tenement building that the RAF, in their wisdom, had arranged for her to stay in. It was worse than anything she had lived in when she had been 'in service' as a scullery maid, and that was saying something. If this was a joke it was not a funny one but she tried hard to hide her emotions from Mrs. Adams who, after all, was only doing her best.

She had provided cots for both children and Joan was, most unusually, lying down in hers. Lily would normally expect her to be standing up and protesting loudly that she was not a baby any more and should be in a proper bed.

"I don't like the look of your daughter!" said Gladys suddenly.

"Well, thank you!" joked Lily, but in truth she did look a little bit hot and bothered. Then she started…

"I want Granddad!" Then, the more she realised that he wasn't there, the more she cried, "I want Granddad!" She looked flushed and unwell and Lily began to get worried.

She felt the child's forehead and realised that she had a temperature. She couldn't believe it!

"I think she has a fever!" said Gladys.

"Oh my God, that's all I need! cried Lily.

There was no choice but to get a doctor to the house. Eventually help arrived in the form of two Red Cross nurses, who bundled the whimpering child and her distraught mother into a car and sped the five or so miles towards Newcastle Infirmary in the black-out leaving Gladys staring into the dark behind them.

Suddenly Lily found that she had no control over events at all. She was tired – and where was Stan when she jolly well needed him?

The toddler was whisked away by an efficient looking nurse and then somebody else sent Lily to a nearby room where she could do nothing else but wait for the outcome along with other anxious mothers. .

"We know what we are doing Mrs. Ratcliff!" a busy and starched looking sister said. "You sit down and we will call you as soon as we know anything."

It had been like a lifetime but eventually somebody did come to tell her that her daughter had a mastoid infection in her ear and that she would have to stay for a few days, or maybe even weeks, in the hospital. It all depended on the results of some tests.

"Mastoid?" cried Lily, "That's serious isn't it?"

"It can be Mrs. Ratcliff," replied the doctor, "if it bursts -it depends on whether we have caught it in time or if we have to operate – the best thing is for you to go home and leave us to it!"

"Can't I stay here?" Lily cried, knowing perfectly well that she would not be allowed to. Hospitals were very strict in such matters.

"Certainly not!" said the sister aghast. She had been shocked at the very idea. There were no facilities to look after weepy mothers – they had enough to do with their offspring!.

There were about thirty other children in high sided iron cots. Most were only tiny and lay there motionless, but one or two were standing up and holding onto the rails like prisoners looking out from behind the bars of a jail. Those that looked as though they might climb over the top were harnessed in with reins.

Joan looked as though she was incapable of climbing anywhere and just sat there staring at all the other children and grizzling. Lily just hoped that none of them had anything infectious and tucked her child tightly under the covers.

"I'll be back when you wake up!" she cried "I promise."

Then she felt the doctor's hand on her arm and a friendly male voice pulled her away and out into the corridor.

"You go home" he said kindly "there is nothing you can do now – come back tomorrow."

She felt rotten having to leave her child behind but she had no choice but to go back to the digs and she was very glad to have Gladys for company. Then – just as she thought that nothing else could happen, she spotted a familiar piece of green silk lying on the floor at the side of Joan's cot.

"Oh bum!" Lily gasped, "I forgot to take her 'ya-ya' with me to the hospital!

"Her what?" exclaimed Gladys.

"Her 'ya-ya'!" She picked up the little piece of rag and put it in her pocket. "She found it in my rag-bag ages ago, and sniffs it when she goes to sleep – I bet my daughter screams the blessed place down when she realises that she hasn't got it."

"She's in the big ward!" a flustered staff nurse said when Lily got to the hospital the following day. "Just down there – don't run!!"

Ignoring the last remark, Lily ran down the corridor and joined with the others rushing through the dark brown swing doors into the huge room which was filled with a mass of whimpering children.

Other cots had been added since she had been there the previous night and now were so close together that the children could touch each other through the bars, and there was an all pervading smell of disinfectant fighting with the odour of wet nappies. In the middle of it all she could see Joan, standing up in her cot, her face crumpled with crying and a plastic bracelet on her wrist, She looked unkempt and in need of a hair wash.

The minute she saw the familiar sight of her mother pushing through the other cots towards her, the crying turned into screaming. She tried to scramble over the bars, frightening the little boy in the next cot to death and creating a chain reaction of screaming round the ward!

"Oh am I glad to see you," said a harassed nurse, "Tell me – what the devil is a blessed ya-ya?"

"This!" said Lily, pulling it out of her pocket, "I am so sorry!"

It was quite amazing to see the effect that one little piece of green silk could have! With a combination of that and the sight of her mother, the child calmed down and the ward went back to normality once again.

"Thank god for that!" exclaimed the nurse, "I wish your landlady would join the twentieth century and get the telephone!"

As it turned out, the doctors had been able to 'disperse' the infection and the threatened 'serious consequences' did not materialise. She still had to stay there a few more days though, with the 'ya-ya', until the fever went. Thankfully the hospital needed the cots so they were as anxious to say goodbye to this very disruptive patient as she was to leave them.

Stan received notice of his posting to the West Country while his daughter was in the hospital and so it was only a matter of days before they journeyed back to Surrey without him. All in all it was an abortive trip to say the least!

The toddler slept most of the way oblivious to her surroundings, except for the background noise of the train and the occasional hefty slamming of doors.. Lily looked out of the windows at the depressing sight of the ruined buildings along the river bank as their final train left Waterloo. When she glanced back along the river to the east she could see the dome of St. Paul's standing proud above the devastation all around it, and blackened by soot. It was always a source of wonderment to Londoners that it had survived the onslaught. Everybody said it was a cross between 'divine intervention' and the unbelievable dedication of the London Fire Brigade!

The train chugged along through Vauxhall and Battersea – by now she was exhausted and it was with complete relief that she and the child arrived unscathed at Woking Station just as darkness began to fall and the blackout came into effect – and how much had Lily seen of her husband after all that? Precious little!

1944 – Gardener's Cottage

The sound of the rooster across the field at Deep Pool farm reminded Lily that it was 1944 now – if nothing else it was one year nearer to it being all over, one way or another! She felt her daughter stir in the bed beside her and it seemed as though she had not had any sleep at all!

Coxhill Manor.

4. *"They were chasing the Germans out of Paris now – weren't they?"*

Autumn 1944 – Gardener's Cottage

Nobody slept late. The rooster was awake at the crack of dawn and made sure that everybody else was too! You didn't need to pull back the blackout curtains to know that it was morning.

"Aw shut up you silly old bird!" grunted Charles as he bent over the sink shaving himself with his cut-throat razor, and leaving just his white bristly moustache intact.

"Stupid thing thinks he's a sergeant major!"

He sharpened the deadly looking object on the big leather strap hanging from the kitchen door and scraped away at his chin as Joan watched with interest.

She was dressed in her new dungarees with the big red J on the front. The fact that they were made out of Granddad's scrubbed trousers made them even more special in her eyes and she was ready for her first job of the morning – collecting the eggs from the chicken coop in the garden.

She ran along behind her grandmother and Alice shooed the birds to one side while they leaned in and carefully picked up the warm eggs from the straw.

Lily envied them their energy and wished she'd had a bit more sleep.

"How many today Joannie?" said Alice.

She counted them into the basin, "one, two, three, four, five, six – we have six today!"

She never missed a chance to teach her granddaughter, if not her numbers, then her letters. Both Lily and Alice could sing the alphabet backwards!

"There's a good girl" said Alice, "Come on and you and I shall have one each of these for our breakfast, – how many do you think that will leave?"

The child counted…

"One, two, four – three!!" came the stumbling answer.

Then Alice burst into song as the chickens scratched around in the dust.

"Come along little chick chicken, lay a little egg for me,

I haven't had one since Easter and I want one for my tea..."

They skipped back into the house as Charles was busy putting on his big black gardening apron to get ready for his day up at Coxhill Manor.

"Do you like your trousers dear? said Alice, nodding in the direction of Joannie.

"Oooh!! Aren't you smart?!" said Charles in mock surprise while she did a 'twirl' for him.

"Whatever next Kate?" he whispered as the infant ran off, "girls in trousers! It's bad enough seeing Rosa in those damn dungarees – it's not ladylike!"

"It's the way of the world dear!" said Alice patiently, "if women do men's jobs then you must expect them to wear the trousers."

"Whatever next?" Charles repeated, mostly to himself, "The world's gone barmy!"

Lily picked up a letter that had just been delivered. It was from Stan and her face lit up.

"He's getting paid as a flight sergeant now." she exclaimed.

"Oh, it will cost sixpence to talk to him." said Charles as he put his grey trilby 'gardening' hat on his head. He was, though, very proud of his son and wasn't very good at hiding it.

She read on. After all the upheavals of the past three years they had decided that it was best not to keep uprooting the child, but Stan was not happy about the threat of the V2s on London and the home counties. The Government were still advising people with young children to take advantage of the evacuation scheme and go to the comparatively safer West Country, out of range of these deadly weapons. There were thousands of older kids who had already been separated from their families for as much as three years.

The village was only twenty miles outside the capital, and just a few miles away from two aircraft factories. There were many occasions when you could hear the thud as they landed nearby, or one could watch as dog-fights went on high up in the clouds above them.

However, Lily wanted to avoid going away yet again even if it did mean being nearer to Stan. She knew from past experience that it didn't necessarily mean she would see him – far from it. As everybody kept saying – 'There *was* a war on!' as if it wasn't quite obvious!

Besides.... they were chasing the Germans *out* of Paris now, weren't they!? It really would soon be over, surely to goodness. Though it did seem that the more desperate the enemy became the more doodlebugs were sent in their efforts to annihilate us.

Lily half-heartedly picked up a duster and went into the bedroom, leaving her daughter trying to help Alice dry the dishes in the kitchen. She couldn't help thinking that her mother-in-law had the patience of a saint! She really wasn't in the mood for cleaning though. The very idea of being evacuated was too much to bear! She had done her level best to be with Stan when he was in this country, despite the difficulties, but everything was always stacked against them. She picked up his photo and 'told him off'.

"What do you think you are asking of me?" she said to the handsome smiling man looking back at her from the picture, "we haven't been back from up North for five minutes!"

Then she heard the familiar sound of laughter coming from the kitchen. She didn't know what the pair of them were up to but it certainly sounded like a lot of fun. Alice never tired of entertaining her granddaughter and she was a different child now from the one that she had been forced to leave in that awful Infirmary. Childhood memories were short – Lily's were much longer and she knew that she would never really forget that trip to Newcastle despite the undoubted friendliness of the people.

Now Stan was down in Wiltshire somewhere. However, Lily reasoned that it was quite possible that she could go down there and then have to come back a week later because it would all be over. It could not go on for ever – could it?

Also, she knew enough about RAF life by now to know that nothing would surprise her any more, especially now that he had got his promotion. They could post him to the other side of the world before she had been there five minutes. It really was a job to know what to do for the best.

Everyone knew, of course, how vulnerable these delightful lanes and gardens of Surrey were though. The very idea of Hitler's army thudding all over them was totally inconceivable. She shivered at the thought, but it was a real prospect – after all it had already happened in the Channel Islands.

Edith, one of Alice's sisters, ran a café in Jersey along with her husband Wilfred, and *they* had been occupied by the Germans since 1940! Nobody could believe it when they heard that Hitler was actually on British soil. Lily hadn't forgotten that Stan had been involved in helping with the evacuation of these Islands just a matter of weeks before he was sent to France. Edith and Wilf had not been among the thousands of people leaving though.

"I am not going to leave my man and my home!" she had said, "Both were too hard come by!"

Then, even if she had wanted to change her mind it became too late.

Churchill ordered that any further efforts at evacuation of the Channel Islands should stop as the troops were needed in the wider scheme of defending the mainland and crushing Hitler. They were still occupied and nobody knew anything about how they were faring.

Lily whizzed around the rest of the bedroom with the duster and walked through into the kitchen that was the centre of all activity. Her spirits were lifted as Joan came in carrying a huge bunch of dead looking dandelions, closely followed by Alice.

"See what we picked!" she said proudly, as if they were gold-dust. "Granny helped me."

Alice was already filling jam jars with water.

"Look Granny, aren't they nice!" she said, "Come on – smell them!"

They smelled awful but nobody cared and all the white sap was coming out of the stalks on to her dungarees, but nobody cared about that either.

"They make you wet the bed!" said Lily, screwing her nose up. She wished it was spring and then there would be something a bit more savoury – like primroses or bluebells.

"No they don't" said Alice, "Don't you take any notice of your mummy Joannie – they are indeed beautiful and all the more so because they are the last of the autumn!" "Come on put them in water and then they won't die!"

Alice and Charles.

She started to arrange the dandelions and the mood brightened immediately. Stan's mother was the dearest and sweetest of ladies and Lily felt that, but for her, she would have gone insane by now.

"Mum!" said Lily suddenly, "Why does dad call you Kate?"

"I don't think he likes the name Alice," she replied, "But I don't care what he calls me, as long as he calls me!"

Lily decided that she was going to be none the wiser and concentrated instead on trying to convince herself that she liked half dead dandelions.

She also tried to put the idea of the V2s and evacuation out of her mind. Like Scarlet O'Hara in 'Gone with the Wind', "she would think about it tomorrow!"

The Indian summer they had been blessed with was all but over and winter was approaching. The days when Joan could play in the meadow at the back of the bungalow were diminishing and the dandelions were few and far between.

Alice made her a 'house' under the kitchen table and she played contently underneath while they got on with their chores. The child, like most in 1944, had no toys, as such. Rationing and the times they were living in prevented anything other than the ones the family had made for her, but she did not miss what she had never had.

She made the best of her motley array of 'dolls', sitting them up under the table, ready to 'have tea' or be taught their A.B.C.! There was a wooden one that Granddad had carved and her mother had made a dress and hat for and also her golly which had been knitted from a pattern by Granny. He had a big round face and a smiley mouth of red felt and she loved him to bits.

She lined them up while Alice went to the back door and looked up into the grey winter sky. She stood transfixed as she watched the intricate patterns and white vapour trails overhead. She couldn't make out the planes – but even her untrained eye could see there was a battle going on with scores of aircraft involved and she hoped that none of them would fall this way!

"Oh when will it all end!?" she asked herself for the umpteenth time.

She felt that the only thing that was keeping the country, including herself, going at the moment were Winston Churchill's speeches but if the war could be won on words alone then the 'Great man' would have won it ages ago!

The sight of these aerial activities made it feel as if she was in a different world to the one she had been born into. She looked down at her grandchild and smiled to herself as she remembered Stanley at much the same age.

He used to play under the table just the same, with a wooden sword and with her vegetable colander perched on his head pretending to be a soldier. He had been oblivious as to the horrors his father was going through in the First World War.

"At least that had been one blessing." thought Alice, "those back home had been mostly unaware of what was going on in the 'first lot'". There had been no wireless to listen to, and the only real news had appeared in dribs and drabs in newspapers stuck on the wall of the Town Hall, It really had been a case of 'ignorance being bliss'.

As each tortuous month went by for the two and a half years that Charles was away Alice had thought she would 'go mad' so she knew what Lily felt like. Now, looking back, she was glad she hadn't known too much. Even now, she didn't know as much about the 'first lot' as future generations would – once it all became pieced together by the experts.

Charles, like many others directly involved, did not speak about his experiences in the trenches. He always said that "He remembered the going off and he remembered the coming back – it was the bit in between that he would rather forget!"

It was different now. Every household had a wireless, and you could even go and see some of the News on film at the pictures. It was surreal to think that you could see the battle for the defence of Malta, which Stanley was involved in, at the local picture house.

"Come on Mum!" the sound of Lily's voice cut through Alice's thoughts. "It's elevenses, last of the tea ration, so come and make the most of it."

Her eyes followed Alice's gaze up to the heavens as the aeroplanes seemed to be taking their fight further away.

"Looks like somebody else is going to get it," said Lily, "we don't want any of them landing on us!"

"Oh let's hope they all keep going on their way and drop in the sea." Alice replied.

Lily turned her attentions to her daughter and peered under the table.

"Hello there, 'knock knock!' – I expect Granddad will be home soon!" she smiled.

Joan came scrambling out from underneath and climbed up onto her own box that she could stand on and look out of the kitchen window where she could see the old man coming across the meadow. Lily saw him first though and quickly made sure her daughter was wrapped up warm with coat and pixie hood.

"I can see him!" the child shouted, "There he is!" and she was gone. Lily was just quick enough to run and overtake her and open the gate before she broke her neck trying to climb over the top of it.

"Granddad, Granddad, Granddad!"

"Careful child, you'll fall down!"

She did, but was up again in minutes and hurtling across the meadow towards his barrow. He marvelled at how much she had grown since they had come back from the north.

"Come on then – jump in." She felt herself being lifted up and put onto the warm sacks and Charles pushed the barrow the rest of the way across the field.

As he was speaking a squirrel came along and sat on its hind legs sniffing the air just in front of them and he stopped and stooped down.

"Hello there!" said Charles in a quiet voice "what are you doing over here young Sally Squirrel?"

"That's a sure sign of winter coming Joannie!" whispered Charles, "She's hiding her food ready to go back and find it later."

"Hello Sally!" said Joan "how are you today?"

"She said that she is very well thank you very much." said Charles.

By now his legs were aching with stooping. He stood up and the squirrel ran off. They got indoors just in time to hear the latest news.

"The first V2 to hit the coast of Britain landed at Hastings at noon….!"

"Oh good heavens alive!" exclaimed Alice as she put his tea on the table, "what have we come to?"

"God knows!" grunted Charles, "but Lily, you and that child really need to go where it is safer – at least Stan can sort things out for you."

"Oh, knowing my luck, I'll get there and he'll get posted to the other end of the country again," said Lily, but she agreed that her father-in-law was right – again!

"I know you are right Dad, but I think I had better take Joan over and see my parents before we go – I feel quite guilty."

"Yes you should young lady," Charles agreed, "make sure you are back before the blackout though".

Alice covered her face in her apron. It was all too much.

It had felt like ages since Lily had seen her parents, but it was such an effort to go over on the bus. Besides, her mother was always busy with her brothers and sisters and there was not a lot of love lost between herself and her father who had both his feet firmly in the nineteenth century. She had yet to forgive him for sending her out into service as a scullery maid, though no doubt he did what he thought was right at the time.

Housewives Choice had started on the wireless and Joan had disappeared under the table again while they drank their elevenses. Then, suddenly, without warning, not even a siren, there was an enormous 'thud', just as if God had dropped a huge weight straight to the ground not far away.

Everything shuddered and the windows rattled and one cracked across. The cups went everywhere and Lily's impending trip to see her own family were temporarily forgotten in the mayhem..

"Oh my God – it's Armageddon!" exclaimed Alice.

They all dived underneath the table with Joan and her toys. At the same time a whirring sound whooshed high overhead and was gone in a split second.

Joan felt her mother grab her and hold her tight against her apron and she knew immediately that she would be all right. There was something about that apron that was very comforting at times like this especially under the big kitchen table. Besides, she was too shocked to protest.

Charles rushed to the door and he could see smoke billowing up not far from the aircraft factory.

"That must have been a V2!" he said. "That's what they were talking about on the wireless – it goes faster than sound – and they are damn well learning to point them to wherever they want them to go!"

As it turned out, Charles wasn't quite correct. The V2's were less than accurate but this, in a way, made them even deadlier.

Alice was aghast! She knew perfectly well that this 'thing' had just landed on some poor souls, but it was the noise afterwards that she didn't understand. It didn't seem right somehow.

"That Kate" said Charles "was the sound following that damn thing over there."

Just for once Alice ignored his continuous use of the word 'damn'! Just for once it somehow seemed appropriate about something that could go faster than sound. Anything that could go faster than sound must be the work of the very devil himself.

Lily couldn't understand what "faster than sound" meant either or how they could guide these weapons all the way from Germany. However, if the allies were liberating Paris then she just hoped that they would jolly well hurry up and get on with it before Hitler finished us all off.

Alice made them all another cup of tea and this time she did not mind Charles pouring it into his saucer.

5. *"It's only thunder..."*

1944 – Hyde Cottage

It was a cold and frosty afternoon when Lily caught the bus to her parents. For her daughter it was just one big adventure and she accepted her other grandparents in just the same way as she did the ones she lived with. In many ways they were similar, and yet very different, although the differences were not apparent to the child. History was certainly being repeated though. She smiled ironically to herself as she lifted the three year old from the bus and cheerily waved to the conductor.

Lily was born at the outbreak of the First World War, and, just like the later generation, and in common with Stan and his sisters, her father did not see her until babyhood had passed by. After initially sharing rooms, her mother moved in to an old fashioned house at the bottom of a long stony cart track in the middle of the farmer's fields. Lily was walking down it now, deep in thought. There had been no running water, no flush toilet. gas or electricity. Even now, as she watched her daughter, alternately running along in front of her or dawdling behind, she marvelled at how her mother managed. She thought she deserved a medal! Hyde Cottage was still lit by gas lamps, there was no plumbing and, until quite recently, all water was drawn from the well.

Her father, Henry Gosley, had come from generations of seafarers, although he was the first *not* to take to that way of life. He, unlike his ancestors, studied accountancy and joined the Army as a regular soldier in the comparative comfort of Pay Accounts. Now, all these years later, he worked as a civilian at the barracks where he had first enlisted. After he came back from the War he and Grace had seven more children. These, as far as Lily was concerned, fell into two distinct groups – the four who were old enough to remember their older sister before she had been put into service but who had now left home themselves for one reason or another, and the three younger ones who only really knew her as an adult.

The former were Harry, her eldest brother, who she rarely saw, Frederick with the RAF in India, Phyllis who she had played with as a child but, like her, had been 'put out to-service' and Frank who was in the Army. She remembered them far better than they her.

The younger ones were Elsie, Bob and Reggie who were still children.

The lane had not changed one jot since she was at school. There was a cornfield on one side, and on the other side an apple orchard. However, she was horrified to see how many craters there were from bombs and how close they had come to the house. In fact, the house had lost nearly all its windows twice already, and many were still boarded up.

Further down the stony old track she saw the, still smouldering, ruins of an aircraft that had 'nose-dived' into the field. Only the tail was intact with the swastika clearly visible. Lily looked aghast at the devastation to the area where she used to play.

She remembered the fun she had with the older three playing in the fields, although her playtime had been very limited. As soon as she was old enough she had been expected to help with the younger ones and rarely had time to herself.

Then, before she knew it, she was whisked away into service with one day off a month. The only exception was when a new baby was due at home and then she had to go and help out until her mother was on her feet again.

Even then she still did not know the 'mechanics' of where babies came from. She realised, of course that it was not the gooseberry bush but nobody had bothered telling her the facts of life. Indeed, she and Phyllis thought babies arrived in the black bag carried by the doctor!

It always seemed that first mother would scrub down the stairs and then the Doctor would arrive. Next thing they knew there was a baby! So it was 'stands-to-reason' – the baby came in the black bag.

But that was their life as it was ten or more years ago – it was *their* normality. By the time Lily was considered 'old enough' to know what life was all about she had already left home and, in the end, it was Alice that had answered all her questions, by which time she was into her twenties.

As she walked along towards the house she could hear the distant rumble of bombs dropping. She was hoping that it might be thunder, but it was some hope and she knew that it would be the right thing to go to the West Country. It was a job to know what to do for the best and she hoped and prayed that another of those awful doodlebug things would not come over while she was outside.

Joan was running along the lane in front of her, oblivious to the smashed up aircraft and smell of smoke and was already banging on the back door of the old homestead. Lily caught her up just as her mother opened the latch.

"Hello Mother!" She kissed her and put down her coat and bag. "You look like you have had some activity down the Lane!"

Lily Grace (who was generally known as Grace to avoid confusion) ushered them in and put the kettle over the kitchen range to boil.

"Hello Joannie dear."

Lily cringed – she had no chance when even her own parents lengthened her daughter's name!

"Yes, we have had some activity" Grace went on, "Phyllis and I and the boys were under the stairs last week! – "Those poor airmen in that plane were killed of course!"

"Where was father at the time?" said Lily.

"Guess?," laughed Grace.

"Huh, I might have known – up at the Barracks I'll bet a bob!" she chuckled, "Anyway, where is the old devil now?"

"Oh, he is in his old 'glory-hole' listening to his records." said Grace nodding her head in the direction of the front of the house. "Best to leave him be."

Lily was in no real rush to go into the smoky old front room that her mother called 'Father's Glory-hole' so she settled down for a chat instead.

She sat back in the chair to enjoy her tea and looked round the familiar old fashioned kitchen with the stone floor where Grace had spent every waking moment since 1915 – the only carpet was in Henry's room. Lily liked to have a few minutes with her mother without the old man puffing away on his pipe and putting in his 'twopenceworth in the background'.

The cottage was very old, and consisted of three ground floor rooms – front to back. The front, and best room, which had a large window looking out to the front garden and lane, was Henry's 'den' or office. The middle room which was the main living area, had no such window for Grace to view the scenery but just a half sized one on the side through which she could see people arriving at the back door which lead into the narrower kitchen – especially little girls who had just run down the lane.

This room contained the old fashioned black kitchen range and the large wooden table and chairs similar to Alice's. However, there was one huge asset which the other Granny and Granddad did not have – a piano!

Grace had learned music when she was very young and her pride and joy was the 'high back' iron framed instrument that filled one wall. It was undoubtedly her lifeline.

Then there was the kitchen with its stone walls and floor which contained the large sink and the back door through which Lily and Joan had just entered.

Upstairs there were just two big bedrooms. Here, at various times, when they were younger and most were at home, they slept 'nose to toe'! There was, therefore, no doubt that it had come as a relief to the younger ones when Lily and Phyllis left home, thus making more room for everyone.

Grace put the tea on the table and settled down in the big wooden chair at the side of the kitchen range and wiped her hands down her flowered overall. In many ways she seemed older than she actually was, – yet she was almost twenty years younger than Alice. However, she never lost her sense of humour and seemed to be placidly resigned to her place in the scheme of things.

"We are going to Wiltshire" announced Lily as she sipped her tea. Then, suddenly aware of the child at her side, "We are probably going to Wiltshire on a little holiday,"

"Oh that will be nice!" smiled Grace, "won't that be nice Joannie?

Joannie wasn't too sure!

"Where's Granddad!?"

"He's through there in his smoky old room!" said Grace mischievously, "go on – you go and find him – go and bang on his door as loudly as you can!"

"Ah well, I suppose I had better say hello!" sighed Lily as the child ran through the passage towards the front of the house to let her grandfather know that they were there.

The door to the den opened and the portly figure of Henry Gosley appeared through a haze of smoke. He gave his daughter a peck on the cheek. He was not the most affectionate of men.

"Hello there Lil!" he smiled, "how are you keeping, – how's Stanley?"

"Oh Stan has been promoted" boasted Lily "He is paid as a flight sergeant now!"

She enjoyed that, although it was slightly exaggerated – Stan was only *acting* flight sergeant, but he *was* getting paid for it and that was the main thing!

Henry had always made it clear that he thought his daughter could do better than the son of a 'mere gardener,' which was ironical coming from a man who didn't mind his teenage girls being scullery maids!

Joan took her other grandfather at face value. He was her Granddad and that was that. She was used to climbing on Charles' knee and expected stories from him, so she treated Henry with the same familiarity. She marched into his den and plonked herself on the stool, where he had just been resting his feet, hardly noticing the smoke or the ash down his tubby chest. She would have sat on his lap if she could have but there was not much room with his belly in the way.

"Mummy says we are going on a holiday!" she announced. "Can you play me one of your music things?"

Henry looked over her head to Lily and raised a questioning eyebrow.

"You play your old records." she said "I'll chat to mother."

He was the proud owner of a gramophone with a wind up handle. Joan didn't quite understand how it worked but she was fascinated because he could put big black plastic plate things on it. Then he had to wind it up, and music would come out. He loved brass bands and his favourite of all was 'Sussex by the Sea,' because that was where his parents came from. In no time at all the music was blaring out and he was singing along.

"We're the men from Sussex – Sussex by the sea....."

It was his afternoon off and he would be going back up to the barracks later on that day. As far as he was concerned his situation was ideal for he was a man who thought mostly of himself.

Grace had long since got used to it and made no complaint, although story has it that she did lose her temper with him more than once.

There was one occasion, in particular, when he was late home for his dinner. She was so angry that she threw the meal across the room with such force that it hit the wall above his head and the contents splattered everywhere! The shocked expression on Henry's face was worth the effort!

She certainly had not always been as placid as she appeared to be now! However, after a houseful of children running about in the most primitive of circumstances, she was quite happy to have her peace and quiet and leave him 'to get on with it'.

She had been an attractive woman in her day – tall and statuesque with dark hair and a beautiful complexion which had been passed on to Lily, but now, understandably, she was losing her slim figure and was going grey. She had, however, somehow, managed to keep her sense of humour and always had a twinkle in her eye. Everyone said that she had the 'patience of a Saint'.

Henry looked older than his fifty-four years, with grey straight hair, parted on the side and combed across his head in a 'comb-over'. He was rotund and, unlike Charles Ratcliff, he enjoyed cigars and alcohol a great deal. He bore a marked resemblance to Winston Churchill.

Both Stan's and Lily's families were self-sufficient and neither Grace nor Alice would dream of buying vegetables or clothing in a shop, even if they had enough coupons. Vegetables were grown and clothing was, for the most part, made by hand.

Henry and Grace Gosley.

In fact, unbeknown to his granddaughter, Henry was probably even more self-sufficient than Charles was, because he killed *all* his own meat! Charles would certainly not be above wringing a chicken's neck if it stopped laying eggs but he would 'apologise' to it while he did so!

"Poor little devil," he'd say as he wrung the bird's neck and then tried to look away while he was doing it! Moreover, he was more likely to stand and 'chat' to a rabbit unless his family were really starving!

Henry and his sons, on the other hand, would be out with a shot-gun over the fields – rabbit, hare, pheasants – they represented meat on the table! They were able to skin them and present them to Grace ready for cooking in the big black pot on the kitchen range. Neither family had need of a dustbin because nothing was wasted and what couldn't be burned on a bonfire was buried in the garden.

Having got Henry to play 'Sussex by the Sea' again and a story about his great uncles who lived in the last century and went to sea and drowned, Joan decided that it was time to go back and see what the ladies were doing and ask that Granny play the piano.

Anticipating the demands from her grandchild, she had already lifted the lid and was ready to play. The metronome on top of the piano was swinging backwards and forwards for them to keep time to.

Joan stood one end to play the 'high' notes – in no particular order – while 'the expert' played 'The Bluebells of Scotland' from some sheet music.

"There you are Joannie," said Grace, "You can play The Bluebells of Scotland now."

She couldn't, of course, but nobody minded.

Lily tied Joan's bows up in her hair a bit tighter and screwed her nose up at the smell of the tobacco which was permeating everywhere. She hated it, but it was the least of their worries just now. She looked at the clock on the wall.

"We'll have to go in a minute Mother" she said "otherwise we won't be back before the black-out, – come on young lady, I'll take you out the back first!"

This was the bit that she dreaded – a visit to the tin toilet. It was just a tin bucket that was emptied every so often by a man with a horse and cart. Lily wasn't over-keen on it either and quickly got the chore over with, making a mental note that, next time, she'd encourage her to 'go behind a bush' if it was just a 'wee'! Again, she wondered how her mother put up with it.

They were just about to leave for the walk up the lane when there was the sound of noisy laughter and arguing and Lily's two young brothers came running in. The youngest, Reggie, was nearly nine with a lean face and straight fair hair. He had a pronounced stutter and so said very little as he went and gave his big sister a quick kiss on the cheek and a brief nod towards his niece.

His older brother, Robert, more than made up for him. He was as swarthy and dark as the other was fair – and as noisy as the other child was quiet. He reminded Lily of her brother Fred who she rarely saw these days.

"Hello Lil!" he greeted, "we got bombed the other day, and I saw some hurricane planes fighting?" Then, as an afterthought, "Hello Joannie."

At his age it was the most exciting of times.

"And did you see the German plane down in the field? I saw the pilot's hand sticking out from underneath and then they came and pulled him out and he was dead!"

"Ugh!" cried Lily, genuinely shocked, "You never stopped and watched?"

"He r – r – r ran away!" stuttered Reggie helpfully.

"No I did not!" retorted Bob.

"Yes you did!"

"Did not!"

The conversation went totally over Joan's head as she had already seen the potential of her two uncles turning up so unexpectedly.

They kept ferrets in a big wooden cage on the wall outside and there was a faint possibility that they might open it and let her look at the animals. Until now they had stayed huddled up in the darkness in their straw.

Only Granddad, Bob and Reggie ever handled the ferrets, which were used for catching rabbits and Granddad was otherwise occupied. He had seized the opportunity of his sons arriving to busy himself getting ready for his visit to the Sergeants Mess.

"No touching!" said Bob as he leaned into the hutch and lifted one out, "He'll nip your fingers off – they are not pets you know!"

He knew just exactly how to hold them by the scruff of the creature's neck leaving the body dangling in mid air, helpless. It had a lovely honey coloured coat but Bob was very careful and only allowed his niece to stroke it for a minute before, expertly, putting it back in it's straw. Lily couldn't help but think that if her daughter actually saw the ferrets in action she might go off them, though everyone ate the rabbit.

"Right come on now!" She was getting anxious. It was a long walk up the lane with a small child and she did *not* want to wait half an hour for the next bus and get back after the black-out.

She gave her brothers a quick peck on the cheek.

"I'll see you soon!" she whispered "You stay out of the way of those old doodlebugs – do you hear me?"

They ran off still arguing about whether Bob had 'run away' or not.

She couldn't help wondering why her father had not insisted on them going away for a while. Many of their age had gone some time ago, but the chances are that he did not want their schooling interrupted. He considered education to be very important for boys, but not for girls who, in his opinion, would just be housewives when they grew up..

Henry emerged, finally, from his den, wearing his best dark suit and with his watch and chain in his waistcoat pocket. Now he looked even more like Winston Churchill than ever..

"Mother won't see *him* again for the rest of the night." Lily thought, "He'll spend the evening drinking with his cronies."

"Come on, I'll walk you both to the bus Lil'!" he said gallantly.

Grace gave Lily a hug and strolled with them down the front path to the lane. On the left, just in front of Henry's window was her little patch of garden. This was her domain away from the kitchen range and in the spring it was a mass of London Pride and Forget-me-nots. Here, Grace stood and watched until they reached the top of the lane and turned the corner onto the main road and out of sight.

Every so often Lily turned round and gave the diminishing figure of her mother a wave but even as she did so there was a rumbling in the distance and the sound of sirens.

"What was that?" said Joan.

"Oh just thunder!" lied Lily, "it's the clouds banging together," she said a little unconvincingly. Joan looked up into the clear blue sky with its white streaks and circles. She wasn't sure whether those were clouds or not, but she accepted what her mother said.

It was a slow trudge along the old dirt track and the bus appeared at the end of the road as they turned the corner at the top and gave a last wave to Grace.

"Take care Lil'," said Henry, as he panted for breath, "and – don't worry – it will all be over soon."

"I hope so Father," she replied.

"I mean it," he went on, "the Germans are beaten and these V2 rockets are like the last shake of a rattle-snake's tail!"

She gave him a big hug. He wasn't a bad person really. He was just firmly stuck in the nineteenth century, and he didn't put her, or Phyllis, out to service out of any malice or because he didn't love them. It was just what he thought was right at the time and their normality.

In any case, she couldn't help thinking that he had unwittingly done her a *huge* favour! After all, if she hadn't started out as a scullery maid she then might never have become a kitchen maid in the establishment where Doris worked, and then she would never have met her beloved Stan.

They climbed on the bus and Joan knelt on the seat beside her and waved to her Granddad while Lily held on tightly to her reins. Then the child turned round and occupied the lady behind them in a deep and meaningful conversation about ferrets, saying the alphabet backwards and hunting for pies.

Lily, meanwhile was deep in thought about the 'whole meaning of life' and how one split second decision, good or bad, in one generation can so influence those in the next!

She gazed out of the window in the increasing gloom. Everywhere looked so dingy and unkempt. The lovely tree-lined road had always had well trimmed hedges and grass, but now people had their minds on other things. There were many houses boarded up and all had tape over the windows. Even the lovely iron railings had been removed from the gardens of the old Victorian houses, that she was so familiar with, as part of the War effort.

The bus took her past the big house where she had first been in service and it looked dreary. It was four stories high and she could see the tiny little window in the roof where she had slept.

"Funny how the scullery maid had the lowest room to work in and the highest room to sleep in." she thought.

She glanced down at her hands and could remember them bleeding because of the amount of washing up she had to do. At least she did not have to put up with that any more.

The lady sitting behind them, having been thoroughly bemused by the art of ferret keeping and pie hunting stood up and bid them both goodbye and Joan settled down into her seat, this time facing the right way.

Gradually, despite her best efforts not to, she began to fall asleep as the bus went down the road towards the Gardener's Cottage. She was older now and much more aware of her circumstances than she had been when they had gone to Sheerness and to Newcastle. Already Lily was beginning to feel rotten about the upheaval ahead and wished she could put it off.

Although Lily was registered for evacuation because she had a child under five, it still took a good few days for all the paperwork and arrangements to take place. There was so much talk that we were winning the war – maybe if she waited until after Christmas it would not be necessary and Stan would be home for good.

However people were still leaving in their droves. It was said that up to 20,000 a day were leaving London and the Home Counties. The streets in the village were eerily quiet. She wasn't going to be able to put it off for much longer.

6. *"I've got Eye-tyes in my vegetable patch!"*

1944 – Gardener's Cottage

After Lily returned from her visit to her parents there were a number of very loud explosions and it was well reported that a V1 had hit the nearby aircraft factory and that the V2's were making more and more hits in the South West corner of Britain and the South Coast. There had also been more letters from Stan and he was arranging to get some time off to come and take her to Chippenham. He knew the place well as he had been there some time now. The bad news was that he was likely to be posted to Egypt. She ignored that bit!

She was concentrating on writing back to him when Rosa poked her head round the door, a smile on her face from ear to ear. Her sister-in-law was almost a female version of Stan – she looked so like him whereas her younger sibling looked more like her mother. Both girls were tall and slim, as he was, and had dark hair like him – but unlike their brother who had the blue/grey eyes of his father, they had the brown eyes of Alice.

"Hey Lil," she cried "Dad's on his way back from the gardens – don't say anything, but just take a look at his face when he comes in – he looks like thunder!!"

"Why? Who's upset him now?"

"He's had some Italian P.O.Ws turn up to work in the gardens," she replied "you can guess how that's pleased him – I don't think!"

Lily giggled and followed Rosa to the kitchen where she could see Charles storming across the field pushing his barrow. Joannie had spotted him too and already she was through the gate and across to meet him, oblivious to his dark mood.

The sight of his granddaughter calmed his rage a bit as he automatically lifted her up, as he had done so many times before, and plonked her into the wheelbarrow to ride the last few yards across the grass.

She jumped out and came running in before him as he put the barrow away, and the ladies tried hard to hide their amusement. Charles being indignant was really an awesome sight. His little white moustache almost quivered in his rage.

Rosa and Doris.

"I've only got some bloomin' eye-tye's in my vegetable patch," he announced. "That's the Government for you, they should be in blood.... (he remembered Joannie nearby) blinking gaol – what is the point of having a Home Guard if they let damn foreign turncoats walk freely around the place anyway?!"

She did not know what eye tyes were, or turncoats for that matter, but she did wonder if they were weeds. She knew Granddad did not like weeds, especially in the vegetable patch.

"Don't worry Dad." giggled Rosa "you can put them among the cabbages where you can keep an eye on them!"

"I'll keep an eye on them all right my girl?" snarled Charles indignantly, "blasted eye tyes – the bloody war would be over and won if they could make up their minds which side they were on!"

"Charles!!" cried Alice as she came in with a basket of dried washing, "language in front of the child."

"They could have been the very ones that have been dropping bombs on Malta!" he went on, ignoring his wife's protests. "They should be behind barbed wire, the same as our blokes are – we are too soft."

"Well at least it tells us one thing," said Lily helpfully, "We must be winning!"

"I never thought if I lived to be a hundred that I would ever have to watch out for bloomin' eye- tyes in Gabriel's gardens."

Then, to press home his point, he thumped the kitchen table with his clenched fist and the cutlery in the drawer rattled loudly. "Never!!"

Rosa and Lily tried hard to keep straight faces. To Charles it was tantamount to feeding the enemy, especially as he had heard all sorts of stories on the news about how British Prisoners of War had been treated, and now here they were, walking freely around Coxhill.

"Now Charles" said Alice quietly, and typically, from the side of the kitchen, where she had started her ironing, "you must be Christian."

"Huh!" he grunted, "*We* didn't start it – if I see any of them anywhere near my greenhouses I will have their giblets out."

Joannie was busy trying to build a tower with some playing cards on the kitchen table. She still didn't know what a 'bloomin eye tye' was, never mind a bloody one, or what connection they had with giblets – she knew what giblets were because Granny boiled them up to make stock

However, the old man could calm down as quickly as he had erupted and by the time Alice and Rosa had put the tea on the table he was back to his normal demeanour.

"He doesn't like the Italians much does he?" Lily whispered to Rosa, as they were doing the washing up afterwards.

"No!" Rosa replied, "perhaps if they had stuck to fighting with us instead of coming down on the side of the Germans, it would all be over by now and we could all live normal lives again."

"You can't blame each individual one though." said Lily generously "they said on the News that some of them don't want to fight with the Germans."

"*Dad* can!" laughed Rosa, – "especially when they can't make up their minds." She finished drying the dishes and started to put them away.

"Actually Lil'" she grinned, "they are very nice – ever so good looking."

"Rosa!" gasped Lily. They both giggled together like a couple of naughty schoolgirls.

Charles had already switched the wireless on and was glued to the News – the Germans had been chased out of France but they were not going down easily.

Despite the 'eye-tyes' in his vegetable patch and the continual threat of the V2's he went to bed that night feeling a bit better than he had for a long time. Maybe it was getting near to the 'end of the end' rather than the 'beginning of the end'.

Lily was already packed when Stan arrived home to take her and the child down to Chippenham to the digs that he had arranged. The celebrations at seeing him again were a bit muted but Charles opened a bottle of Port. He also bought Joannie back a present from the village. It was a magic colouring book. To her it was a wondrous thing, especially when her father showed her how to put the water on the paint brush and bring out the magic colours.

There was one very special picture of Noah's Ark that caught Joan's eye. Noah was holding a dove high up on one hand and looking across at a big rainbow.

"Don't put too much water on your brush." said Stan "see here, squeeze it with your fingers and paint it carefully."

As she did so, the colours came alive like magic and the rainbow showed up red, orange and green and mauve.

Despite all his efforts Stan was still a stranger to her but she allowed him to show her what to do before running off and showing it to Granny and Granddad first.

"Who's that in the picture Granddad?" she asked.

"Well, that is old Noah and he is looking up at the rainbow," replied Charles.

"What's a rainbow?"

"Oh goodness, he is going to get twenty questions now!" giggled Lily to Stan.

"A rainbow is what happens after it has been raining and then the sun comes out and shines on the raindrops," he replied with a patience that few in the room had seen before. "God showed the rainbow to Noah to remind him that all will be all right in the end. See, Joannie, Noah thought that the world was going to be flooded and be spoilt so he marched all the animals into the Ark…"

Most of what he was saying was going totally over the three year olds head.

"What's an Ark Granddad?"

"It's a sort of boat," carried on Charles manfully, ignoring the giggles coming from the other side of the room, "He marched all the animals into the boat two by two," he went on, "but the world wasn't spoilt after all, and God showed the rainbow to Noah to remind him to trust him."

"Will I ever see a rainbow Granddad?"

"Of course you will my child" Charles went on, "you will see lot's of rainbows before you are ninety."

The book was designed in such a way that the pages could be pulled out along a perforated edge and put into a frame or turned into a calendar. She was very impressed with her efforts and insisted that the page be torn out and the picture propped on the mantelpiece for everyone to see.

"This is a lovely rainbow," said Charles, "I shall keep this for ever to remind me that things will be all right in the end."

Despite Charles' stories about Noah, Joan was not very happy at all about going to Chippenham. She had sensed from the amount her mother started packing that this was not going to be a very short holiday and she could still vaguely remember going away on the train and the bars of a hospital cot the last time a big case like that was packed.

Besides, Granddad had said that, one of these days, he would take her down to the gardens where he worked. She followed him across the field every day, and met him when he came home, but he always firmly shut the iron gate on the other side behind him.

"No, you run back to your mother now, you are not quite big enough yet Joannie" he would say – "I'll take you when you are four."

When she saw Lily packing she thought it was time he was reminded again.

"When can I come down the gardens Granddad, I want to see the bloomin eye-tyes!"

Charles laughed,

"I am certainly not taking you down the gardens while the eye-tyes are there my girl!"

"Charles!!" The exclamation came from where Alice was using the leavings to make more mash for the chickens. "Don't be so unchristian!!"

"Well!" he retorted "bloomin' eye tyes."

Now it looked as though her trip to the gardens would have to wait even longer, because she and mummy were going away and every so often she heard somebody talk about being 'vackerated'.

Strictly speaking they were not being evacuated. Joan did not have a label to wear and she was going with her mother. Moreover it was her mother's choice, but they still called it that anyway.

"It won't be for long!" said Charles "and then you can come home and then I promise I will take you up the gardens one of these days, eye tyes or no bloomin eye tyes!" He was teasing Alice now!

"Charles!" The cry came from the kitchen again as Stan and Lily dissolved into laughter.

Alice had been trying since 1907 to turn him into a 'gentleman'. It was a lost cause. Now, all she was doing was 'going through the motions'. He was a rough diamond, but a diamond for all that and, in reality, she wouldn't have him any different, and neither would anyone else.

At least it was a more straightforward journey this time, consisting of a bus to Guildford and then the train through to Chippenham. Lily would certainly miss the self-sufficiency of both Stan's parents and her own and she hoped above anything else that they would not be away for long and that where they were going they would have a vegetable patch. She had missed the fresh vegetables when they were in digs at Newcastle.

Charles and Alice watched them as they got on the bus and Alice put a little bag of sweets in Joan's hand – they represented her rations for a fortnight. They were soon joined by Rosa.

"You take care Joannie dear!" she said "and we shall see you again really soon."

There were lots of hugs and kisses and reassurances and then they were on the bus looking back at the little group at the gate who were waving at them until they were out of sight.

"Are we going to see my other Granny and Granddad?" said Joan.

"Not today!" said Lily, "But you can go to school, won't that be nice?" Joan was not so sure about that either and the tears came as she realised that they might not be coming back today after all. Despite the luxury of sweets it was not a very happy journey for anyone.

Alice, Charles and Rosa waved at the disappearing bus and then went into the house. Alice already had her apron over her face.

"Put the kettle on woman!" said Charles gruffly, "I need a cup of tea before I go back down the gardens – preferably with a brandy in it!"

He settled down in his chair and switched the radio on just in time for the news. It was news to gladden the heart.

".....The Allies have taken Belgium and the port of Antwerp is open for merchant shipping."

He punched the air.

"Now *that* is what I want to hear Kate!" he said to Alice "I feel better already!"

Rosa had already changed into her dungarees to go back to work, and came in to the kitchen just in time to see her, usually morose and gruff father, jumping up and down with glee and swinging her, still tearful, mother around the room.

"It will be all over by the spring, you see my gal!" he cried.

"Oh, I don't mind going back to work now!" said Rosa, "not that there is much to do in this weather."

It was true, there wasn't all that much to do. Of course there was kale and winter cabbage to cut, but there really wasn't enough to keep them busy at the moment, never mind Italian Prisoners of War as well. Charles hoped that soon they would be shipped on the next boat home! They were just two out of thousands of German and Italian P.O.W's in Britain. As far as he was concerned we had enough to do keeping our own population fed, never mind them as well. They needed to go back to their families just as surely as our own boys needed to be returned to us.

Alice had propped Joannie's water splodged rainbow picture up on the mantelpiece.

"She did it for you," she said, "We'll call it 'Granddad's Rainbow' from now on!"

He grunted in acknowledgement, pulled his grey trilby hat over his bald head, put on his black gardening apron and tied the string round his waist. This time he strode off to work without his 'shadow' hitching a lift in his wheelbarrow as far as the iron gate. Christmas was approaching and he just hoped that 1945 would be the end of it all.

Winter 1944 – Chippenham

By the time the bus reached Guildford, Stan, Lily and Joan had been joined by hoards of other young mothers and their children who were going in the same direction. They were, actually, quite a cheerful bunch that boarded the train to

Chippenham and Joan had plenty to occupy her mind to stop her from remembering how miserable she was supposed to be.

There were hundreds of soldiers, sailors and airmen, all in uniform like Stan, and many of them were American or Canadian. All had a tale to tell, if not about where they came from, then about their involvement in the liberation of Paris. A few of them were black and it was difficult, even for the adults, not to stare – a black person was a rare and unusual sight – but they were obviously used to the uninhibited stares of small children and appeared to be unfazed by it

In what seemed like no time at all the train pulled into Chippenham station and there was no shortage of willing hands to help the ladies with their children and their luggage. It was cold and it was starting to snow but they had got there long before the black-out and that was the main thing.

"When are we going home?" said Joan, the minute they left the station.

Lily didn't think she would get the request quite so soon.

"Oh, in a few weeks."

She wasn't too impressed but allowed herself to be picked up and given a 'piggy-back' by her father and accepted some candy from one of the black Americans who called himself Samuel.

At first she was a bit wary as she had never seen a black man before – neither had Lily for that matter – but his friendliness, and the sweets, did much to overcome the initial strangeness of seeing a black face for the first time.

It wasn't far on the RAF bus to the outskirts of Chippenham and 24 Palmer Street, where the digs were, but Lily was painfully aware that this brief time with Stan was going to be very short lived. He had done well to get the time off at all and would have to report back to camp before long. She made a mental note that the RAF must owe him months of leave – all leave had been cancelled throughout the duration of the war with only the odd day snatched here and there.

They arrived at an old Victorian style house, three stories high, in a tree-lined street. The owners were Mr and Mrs

Stephens. Once again Lily found that they were on the top floor.

"Oh why do I always get the blessed roof" she thought inwardly, as she climbed up the stairs behind Stan with Joan reluctantly following behind.

As it turned out, it was quite a nice room with a double bed and a tiny recess to the side with a camp bed in. Not that the latter would be used much – Joan had already decided that she was going to share with her mother as usual no matter what.

There was also a dresser with a china bowl and jug for washing on it. The only trouble was that the water had to be carried up three flights of stairs from the kitchen. Lily sincerely hoped it would not be for long otherwise she would either fade away or become very dirty!

"I'll have some dinner ready for you in half an hour!" Mrs. Stephens shouted up the stairs, and I'll need your ration books."

Although Lily could not wait for it to be all over, she did admire the people that took in evacuees. It was not a job she would like to have done herself though they did get paid for it. Their hosts, like many in the street, were living in cramped conditions on the ground floor while the rest of the house was given over to the lodgers.

She also found that she was not the only evacuee in the house. There was also a girl called Vera staying there and she had a young daughter, called Ann, who was much the same age as Joan. Her husband was also stationed at RAF Hullavington but had recently been sent off to North Africa.

"Oh, I am beginning to forget what he looks like," she moaned. "I should think this damned war has ruined thousands of marriages."

Once again Lily counted her blessings. At least Stan was with her now although the war had done it's best to ruin things, especially between 1939 and 1943, and it was not over yet. She was, however, determined that neither Hitler, nor anybody else for that matter, was going to spoil things for her and her husband. She would wait for as long as it took even if she did have to have a grumble from time to time.

Like most people, the Stephens relied on self-sufficiency, so the dinner consisted of the inevitable rabbit stew with potatoes cooked on the kitchen range. It was tasty though and Lily was grateful for it. It was amazing what you could do with some vegetables and an Oxo and they were kind enough to include Stan. For Lily it was almost like normality to have him at the dinner table but it did not last long.

He looked up at the clock and got up from the table, went over and gave Joan a kiss and then the child realised that this man, who she was beginning to get used to, was off again. Her mother went with him to the door.

"I've got to go or I'll have the boss after me," he said "must try and catch a bus before the black-out." Then he was gone again with promises that he would be back soon. Once again he was just a photo at the side of her bed.

Mr. Stephens was an ARP Warden and very particular about closing the curtains and putting the shutters up so that not a chink of light appeared on the outside of the house. It was his job to go out and check. His wife said that people could hear him shouting "Put that light out" right across the town.

He was also very particular about the children having gas-masks. Lily had steadfastly tried to avoid this up until now. She recalled how she tried to put Joan into a 'baby' one back in 1942 when she was at Sheerness but without a lot of success. It was like a coffin and you had to pump it all the time because, of course the baby couldn't do it for herself.

Now he was offering them 'grown up' type masks but because the children were under seven they were shaped like Disney characters.

"I've seen it all now!" thought Lily.

"Here you are," he said triumphantly, as he offered them two small brown boxes. "It's Mickey Mouse!"

They had, of course, come from the Americans, but as neither child had ever seen Mickey Mouse before it was, to a certain extent, lost on them.

Vera opened her box and pulled out a small coloured gas mask with ears as the children looked on perplexed.

"You have to take it to the school!" said Mr. Stephens, It was certainly a novelty.

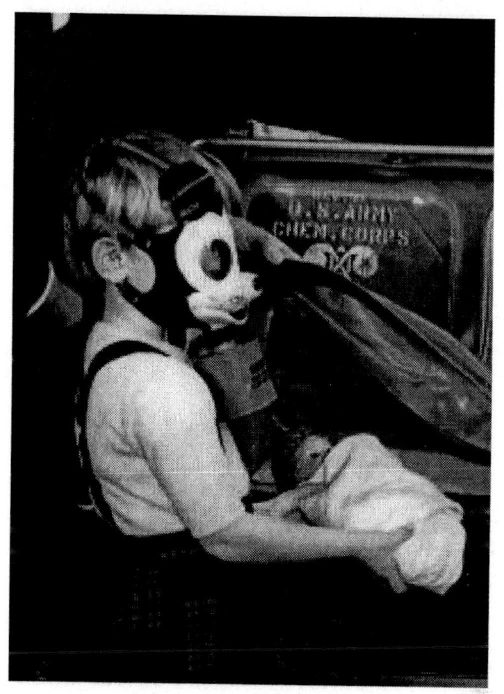

Micky Mouse gas mask.

At first the children were both happy to sit side by side at the dinner table wearing the things and looking totally surreal. However, once they realised that they couldn't eat, the novelty wore off.

"I don't like it!" said Ann, "it smells!"

It did too and when the children breathed in and out so the rubber did as well and looked quite grotesque. Lily and Vera packed the gas masks back in the boxes and hoped that they would not be needed. Then they thanked Mrs. Stephens for their meal and offered to do the washing up.

"No, don't you worry about that my dears!" she replied "George will do it." She looked across at her husband.

"Well, what is the use of having a dog and wagging its tail yourself!" she laughed, "Anyway you can make up for it later."

George Stephens was way past the age for being in the armed services, but like Charles, he still wanted to do his bit. He finished off the washing up as they all wiped, and then put his tin hat on and went off to check the black-outs.

He covered the front lamp of his bike with the lid of a cocoa tin with a just a small hole pierced through it to show the smallest pinprick of light. He could clip it on and off at will and it saved taping the lamp every night. If there was any sign of enemy aircraft even the pinprick was covered up.

Lily made a mental note that she might suggest that to her father-in-law when he went off on his bike to his Home Guard when it was dark. It just might stop him falling in the ditch.

Vera and Lily filled their jugs with warm water from the kettle and together with their children, climbed the never-ending stairs to their rooms.

"I've heard that there are some public baths here somewhere." panted Vera, "I'll use them if I can!" It sounded like a good idea.

She and her daughter were as blonde as Lily and Joan were dark and Ann had beautiful curls just like Shirley Temple.

They bid each other goodnight and Lily and Joan went into the bedroom on their own. Tomorrow the children would be starting school. Both the women had notes to take to the kindergarten in the town and this was something to really look forward to just for a change.

Joan was up bright and early. Her upset at being taken away from her grandparents had faded with the excitement of going to nursery school. Lily had made her a new skirt and knitted her a warm jumper from an unpicked one of her own and she felt ready for anything.

Even though she was still not yet four she could read one or two words and say her alphabet backwards – well, halfway backwards anyway, and she could count – nearly.

They were all able to wash at the sink downstairs and go to the toilet at the bottom of the yard. Mrs. Stephens had made a big bowl of porridge but Lily couldn't help but wish for the day when she could feed her own daughter in her own kitchen. How long that would take she did not know at all.

The snow had all but melted and a watery sun was trying to poke through as Vera, Lily and their children walked down the road to the small Kindergarten.

The head teacher was a tubby middle-aged lady called Mrs. Williams, although all the children called her 'Miss'. She had steely grey hair and glasses on the end of her nose. Ann and Joan were taken off to play in a toy house while 'Miss' took the particulars from the two parents.

She told them that her husband was a prisoner of war in the Far East. That was really bad news because, although the war seemed to be drawing to a close in Europe it was not quite the case in the Far East, so Mrs. Williams had plenty to worry about.

Lily felt very sorry for the woman. There had been awful stories reaching the newspapers about the people in the Japanese Prisoner of War camps. Some said that they were worse than the Germans if that could be believed.

"There is always someone worse off!" she thought. "We don't have to look very far."

Mrs. Williams informed them that the children could have sandwiches and would be at the school most of the day. It wouldn't be for many days though. Christmas was just around the corner. In fact, they were so pre-occupied in the toy house that they hardly turned round when the time came for Vera and Lily to leave.

"Huh! I don't think they are going to miss *us* much!" said Vera as the two women shut the school gate behind them without their offspring giving them a backward glance.

There were about fifty children in the Kindergarten ranging from three to five, with three teachers.

Joan and Ann were thrilled at being at school. 'Miss' showed them where they were to hang their coats and they had their own pegs with their names underneath written in big letters and everyone hung their gas masks on their pegs. Some children had ordinary masks, but most of the very young ones had Mickey Mouse and some had Donald Duck.

They were taken into the school hall where they had to stand with the others and sing, "There's a friend for little children above the bright blue sky." and then the head teacher welcomed them.

Joan had never seen so many children of her own age all in one place at the same time and was a bit overawed by it all. Then they were shown their classroom where they met their teacher, a youngish lady with ginger hair called Miss Paget. She clapped her hands to get their attention..

"Now, now children, silence please because we are going to learn to sing 'Away in a Manger.'

Very little fuss was made out of Christmas as it was quite clear that there would be many children who would not get a visit by Santa Claus. Instead they were told about the Nativity and the baby Jesus and it was left at that.

On the rare occasions when Stan managed to come on a visit Joan, very reluctantly, had to sleep in the recess which she did not like one bit. Then, just as she was starting to get used to him again he arrived with some 'good news and bad news.' He would be able to spend a couple of days at Christmas with them but, the bad news was that, as expected, he would be off to Egypt.

She wondered why her mother kept walking around saying, "I knew it!" over and over again.

"I knew it!" she exclaimed to Vera, "I *knew* it."

Lily was very tempted to just 'up sticks' and go back to Chobham but the reports of the V2's were getting even more alarming. There was talk that they, alone, had killed over 2,000 Londoners. It was very easy to get lulled into a sense of false security down in the West Country, although there was always the overriding fear that Hitler might invade. Then nobody would be safe anywhere.

Everyone made the best of things during the festive period. Stan, despite the intermittent snow and blackout managed to get over to Palmer Street. He even bought a present – a dolls' tea-set. It had blue flowers on it and had a milk jug and sugar bowl and a teapot.

Lily wondered where on earth he could have got such a thing from because there was nothing in the shops. In fact, he had purchased it from one of the Americans who appeared to have brought all sorts of things with them that were unavailable in England, from Mickey Mouse gas masks to candy bars.

Vera found some orange squash and put it in the teapot and the two little girls had fun pouring 'tea' for anyone brave enough to drink it. Stan also bought a bottle of sherry and a chicken and between them all they managed to have a nice dinner. It was always the way though – just as soon as he was starting to bond with his daughter, so he had to go.

He tried not to feel too bitter about it. Like Lily, he had to count his blessings but he had missed his child's first smile, her first tooth, her first step – even calling him daddy – and now she was old enough to go to kindergarten. It would be a saint who did not feel bitter.

Then, as he watched the children playing with the tea-set, he thought of all the 'poor buggers' that had been in his billet in Malta. They had *all* died. They had no chance to see their families or to go anywhere – Egypt or otherwise. He had been spared.

Besides, as far as he could see, it was just a clearing up operation now. As long as Lily stayed in Chippenham until we were really sure it was all over, as his dad had said, "Things *would* be all right in the end."

Winter 1944 Gardener's Cottage

Back at Chobham Charles adjusted his 'rainbow' picture on the mantelpiece as they listened to the sound of sirens in the distance. He peeped outside and looked up into the starlit sky, only to see the pencil thin streaks from the searchlights reaching up to pick out any enemy bombers.

"Blasted Germans!" he exclaimed.

There was certainly a raid going on. You could hear the sound of the aircraft droning overhead. He toyed with the idea of taking Alice and Rosa down to the air raid shelter, but it was cold and miserable and no damn German was going to make him give up his bed.

He stalked off to his bedroom with some very un-seasonal thoughts in his head about what he would like to do to the Germans and the Eye-Tyes, never mind the Japs'!

Alice had heard it all a million times before.

What nobody in the household knew, until the following day, was that on that very night in London, during Midnight Mass, St. Paul's Cathedral had all its windows blown out with the force of a V2 landing nearby. The choir continued singing and the Cathedral walls remained intact. It was like an omen – or a miracle.

In the morning Charles and Alice went to the service at St. Lawrence Church.

Even after all this time it still seemed strange trudging down to the village without the sound of the bells ringing. Everyone longed to hear them again, but there would be none of that until it was all over.

There was a very large congregation of villagers and everyone sang defiantly, almost as if they wanted Hitler and his cronies to hear them sing 'Oh Come all Ye Faithful' across the channel. As the congregation began to sing the last verse of the final hymn the Vicar moved to the door ready to wish people Seasons Greetings on their way out.

"Happy Christmas, Charles, Alice,!" he smiled, giving them a warm shake of the hand as they came down the aisle.

"Can you say an extra prayer for old Stan, Reverend?" muttered Charles, "I don't think 'him upstairs' is listening to me."

Alice 'bristled' at his side! Her efforts to try and refine her husband had fallen on stony ground – yet again!

"Oh he is Mr. Ratcliff, he is," replied the Vicar. "Everyone says it will all be over in a couple of months."

"The Reverend has a difficult job in these times," said Alice as she adjusted her best hat and nodded to her friends as they walked through the churchyard and back along the deserted road to the Gardener's Cottage.

The King was due to speak on the wireless in the afternoon and exactly on the hour of three, the National Anthem was played and Charles leapt to his feet, a glass of sherry in his hand. Rosa and Alice followed suit and toasted the Sovereign. George VI had a terrible stutter but it didn't matter. They felt heartened when he had finished speaking as it was a rousing cry to the British people to stand fast and not be dismayed.

"God bless him!" said Charles.

Then he looked towards the mantelpiece where photos of Alice's parents and his own were on display, together with Joannie's painting.

"And God bless *them* too!" he said "Thank goodness they were spared all this Kate!"

"I'll agree with that!" said Alice, looking at the old faded black and white photos.

There was one of her parents, Sarah and Joshua, posing in the fashions of the turn of the century when they were taken. Joshua was wearing his high topped hat and frock coat and Sarah her long black taffeta dress. At the other end of the mantelpiece was a sepia picture of Elizabeth and the old 'turnip top' John Ratcliff. All had been born in the 1850's and all were now dead.

"Yes, God bless them" said Rosa, who could just about remember them.

"And God bless Stan on his posting to Egypt" said Alice, "and keep him safe,"

"Amen to that," said Charles, "I'll drink to that one."

Winter 1945 – Chippenham

Lily quite envied Stan going off to Egypt whilst she was trudging about in the snow and trying to 'enjoy' making snowmen. She and Vera took turns in taking the children to school and soon the first days of 1945 were slipping away.

Just to add salt into the wound she received her first letter from Stan containing a photo of himself in his tropical gear and showing off his muscles. He did look handsome.

"Look at this Joan!" she said as she put it by the bed, "Look at this lovely picture of daddy."

She vaguely recognised him but he looked different standing there in shorts and open necked shirt so showed little interest. He was a stranger again.

7. *Everyone Sang "Rule Britannia"*

Spring 1945 – Chippenham

The children loved their school despite having to run to air raid shelters every time the siren went off. Very soon they had their own reading books about 'Little Black Sambo,' and all around the room were pictures of a little boy who looked just like her golly. He had a smiley face and a mop of curly hair and he was doing whatever it said in the legend underneath – 'Sambo jumps', 'Sambo skips', 'Sambo swims'.

Their books had brightly coloured pictures of Sambo on each page, always wearing his brand new red coat and blue trousers and purple shoes, with the story of how the nasty tigers took his clothes and then chased one another round and round the palm tree until they melted into butter. Then his mother made cakes with the butter and Sambo got his clothes back. Everyone enjoyed the story and eventually knew it by heart. Children and teachers alike had yet to be taught that such stories were 'in bad taste' and even the black American and Canadian soldiers billeted in and around the area accepted them with the same innocence and spirit as those who learned to read with them.

They treasured their stories and so many of them could read simple sentences by the time they were four. To the smaller ones he was as real as their best friend and they tried to behave themselves because he would try to do so, although not always succeeding.

"Come on" a teacher would say, if she wanted a child to drink their milk, "drink it all up like Sambo does – he's a good boy."

The best bit of the day as far as many of the nursery children were concerned was morning playtime when they got their milk and a small tin of Ovaltine tablets. They were in a little round orange tin and extremely tasty to youngsters who were deprived sweets because of rationing! In truth they were an extra supply of vitamins but they didn't know that.

In the afternoon every child had to take an hours nap, sitting at their desks and, hopefully, falling asleep on their arms. It didn't always work that way but it gave the teachers a bit of peace if nothing else! In this way, for the children at least, the time passed by and the days became weeks and soon it was February and the War, for the Germans, was being well and truly lost!

"Allies bomb Dresden. Allies bomb Dresden" shouted the paper boy as Lily and Vera walked home from the school one day with their daughters. "Allies bomb Dresden! Over 100,000 killed!"

"Oh my word!" gasped Lily, "all those people!"

They walked into the house where Mr. and Mrs. Stephens had already heard the news.

"Run upstairs girls and get your playthings on!" said Vera. The two children raced each other upstairs oblivious to the significance of the latest news.

"Well, that's it now!" said Mr. Stephens, "they won't come back from that surely!"

Lily thought it was just awful. How many more people must die? It went into millions now.

The girls came downstairs clutching their latest pictures to colour. They sat down at Mrs. Stephens' table with their colouring pencils and concentrated hard on their efforts.

"Oh that's lovely!" lied Vera, when they both triumphantly held their pictures up for inspection.

Mr. Stephens did not let the bombing of Dresden put him off his duties of making sure everyone stuck to the blackout though. It was dark early and he went off on his rounds while his wife finished off getting the dinner.

It seemed that the more we appeared to be beating the Germans, the more they used the V1s and V2s in desperation. The entire household listened attentively to the News to hear what was going on in London. It was very eerie to hear about these things that could go faster than sound, hitting the

South West and killing, sometimes, hundreds of people in one go. They only had to perfect the range of the things and then no-one in England would be safe. However Stan's letters were certainly optimistic.

"I will be home soon!" he wrote *"it is all over bar the shouting. Don't worry, I'll survive, It is a lot better here than Malta I can tell you."*

Vera too got letters from her husband George. He was also talking of coming home in the not too distant future.

Lily still felt very tempted to just go back to Chobham, but she resisted the urge. Everyone was being advised not to do so until Hitler had surrendered. He may have something up his sleeve that nobody knew about!

"Maybe a ruddy V3" said Vera sarcastically.

She thought about all those back home and hoped they would be all right.

The snows had melted and the first snowdrops were poking through when Joan saw her first real rainbow. It was the middle of March and the children had been cooped up indoors all weekend because it had been raining on and off. Then, on Sunday morning, it stopped as suddenly as it had started and Lily and Vera decided to take the children out over the fields to let them run about.

It was Lily that spotted it first, the minute they had stepped out of the front door. The sun had come out with a vengeance although there were still some spits and spots of rain, and there, seemingly filling the whole sky was the clearest and perfect rainbow that she had seen for a very long time.

"Joan, Joan, Ann, quick, run!!" she shouted.

The children rushed down the stairs, almost sliding on their bottoms, closely followed by Vera. Joan stopped short at her mother's side and looked up. Lily didn't need to point it out. It was a wondrous sight.

"A rainbow just like Granddad said," she gasped "just like my painting book!"

They all walked down the street together and the rainbow seemed to move with them. The children could not take their eyes off it and it was all their mother's could do to stop them from falling over each other as they both stared upwards.

"It will be like Noah!" said Joan "that's telling us that everything will be all right, Granddad said so."

For the first time in a good many years Lily really, genuinely, felt as though everything *would* be all right – especially if her father-in-law said so.

Gradually the colours began to fade. The little girls ran over the hills and picked coltsfoot and snowdrops. Vera tossed back her blonde hair in defiance.

"No damn German is going to take over us!" she said, "it won't happen!"

The two women sat down on their coats and watched the children playing for a while. It was hard to believe as they sat in the spring sunshine, that, not too far away, people were still dying. 100,000 people had lost their lives in one bombing raid by the RAF on Dresden alone – it was hard to take the figures in never mind relate it to human beings.

The newsboys were out on the streets again when they all strolled back to Palmer Street..

"The Allies have crossed the Rhine into Germany!" shouted one young boy, "come and read all about it, "Allies are taking Germany!"

"Hooray!" shouted Lily and grabbed a paper, "Bloody hooray!"

Lily never, *ever,* swore!

Spring 1945 – Gardener's Cottage

Charles Ratcliff adjusted the picture of his rainbow on the mantelpiece and smiled at his own reflection in the old fashioned mirror over the top. Most of the news was good news now. Most – but not all. The enemy were still finding a few rockets from somewhere and there was still a war going on in the Far East.

"Nothing doing much now!" Stan had written to his parents, *"Looks like they are sending us off to Palestine soon and then 'home James and don't spare the horses!"*

Alice watched Charles as he adjusted the picture. It was really just a splurge of colours all running into one another, but he had carefully put a coloured 'frame' of sticky-tape around it and there it stood at the side of the clock.

"It's almost safe for them to come home now!" she said, reading his thoughts.

"Not until peace is declared!" Charles replied, "You never know with these swine. Some of this news might be just to confuse the enemy."

He sat down and had his porridge and then put on his gardening apron ready for work listening to the wireless at the same time. Alice, who was starting to go a little deaf, began singing as she did the washing up.

"Shh! woman" he grunted, "It's the News!"

She was starting to get heartily sick of it but until peace was declared she would listen as carefully as Charles did.

> *"Information is just reaching us that Mussolini has been shot dead....!"*

Charles allowed himself a hearty cheer, and he lifted Alice up and swung her round.

"That'll teach the bloomin' eye tyes!" he chortled.

Actually he was all 'bluster' over the eye-tyes, as he called them. He had grown quite attached to them. They were only 'kids', and under any other circumstances he would have made them more than welcome in the gardens and his home.

"Everyone was obeying orders in this damn war!" he had thought, "it wasn't *their* fault that their government were turncoats."

He put his wife back down on 'terra firma', and marched across the field to work with a spring in his step. He went through the iron gate and in to the rose garden. At least it used to be the rose garden – now it was all made over to the vegetables and the two Italians were already at work weeding round the early lettuces.

They spoke very little English and Charles spoke no Italian, but they managed to communicate with sign language and pigeon English to each other. Rather than try and pronounce their names he called them both 'Alfonso'! They stood up and stretched their backs.

"Hello Alfonso," said Charles to them both, "Nice day!"

He wasn't sure if they had heard the News. It was unlikely. They and other P.O.Ws occupied some purpose built Nissan huts out at Merrow, near Guildford.

"Looks like they have shot your boss, Mussolini!" said Charles. He did a shooting gesture with his fingers and said again "Mussolini shot!"

They obviously hadn't heard the news but their reaction was not what he had expected! As soon as they realised what he was saying they were jumping for joy and hugging each other, and then, to his amazement, they hugged him. They were delighted to see the back of Mussolini.

"Oi, watch the lettuces!" Charles cried, "you are trampling all over the bloody things!"

He left them to their celebrations and walked towards the kitchens. The news had reached Cook all right, and they had just been joined by Christopher Gabriel himself for a glass of sherry.

"He was shot by his own people!" said Mr. Gabriel, "and then the body hung upside down on a gibbet!"

"Oh my goodness!" exclaimed Rosa, who had just joined them.

"Good job too!" said Cook with feeling, "string him up like the animal he is!"

"All we want now is to hear that Hitler has gone the same way!" said Mr. Gabriel.

Their employer was much the same age as Charles, having been the owner of the house since 1919. Master and servant had worked together ever since and they had a healthy respect for each other.

"Oh you do not know what I would like to do to Hitler!" exclaimed Charles.

"Oh I do Ratcliff!" snarled Mr. Gabriel, "believe me I do!"

Having lost his son John in the war just a year earlier, the end of the war brought no relief from the anguish that Christopher still felt.

"Come on Rosa!" cried Cook suddenly, "have a sherry!"

Within minutes most of the household had gathered in the big kitchen, including Mumford the Butler and Mrs. Gabriel. Eventually though, Charles and Rosa took their leave and made their way to the greenhouses. There was still rationing, the war had not ended yet, and Stanley was not yet home. However, Stanley, who was exactly the same age as John, was still alive, so there were blessings to be counted as well as seeds to be pricked out into boxes.

The last they saw of the Italians was as they left that evening. They never saw them again, and presumed that they had joined the hundreds of others being sent back home.

"Not" Charles thought to himself, "A privilege that had been afforded to *British* servicemen just yet!"

He bumped into his employer again, later in the day, when he was out walking his bulldog, George.

"Well, it's all great news Ratcliff!" he smiled. "Sit – George!"

He had always called Charles by his surname and Charles had always called him 'Mister'. They were not going to change – they were both from a different era in a rapidly changing world.

"Yes, Mister Christopher!" said Charles, "Only a matter of time now!"

"It will be good to have your boy back!" he went on. "Don't forget Ratcliff, he has a job with me any time."

Charles was gratified. His employer owned a very successful timber and creosoting company handed down through generations of Gabriels.

"Thank you Sir!" he replied, genuinely pleased.

Charles and Alice came from a rapidly passing 'Victorian' ethos of 'upstairs and downstairs' and 'everybody knowing their place', but neither of them had ever had any cause for complaint about how they had been treated by the 'gentry' nor were they ever jealous of them.

George sat patiently at the side of his master while the two men launched into talk about what vegetables to plant for the summer.

"Ah don't worry Ratcliff!" said Mr. Gabriel, "You'll be able to plant roses again before long!"

"You can't eat roses Sir," he replied.

"This is true!" laughed his employer.

The two men parted company and Charles made his way across the top of the drive and through into the field to see what his bees were up to.

Between the back drive and the field was a narrow strip of trees and shrubbery in which Charles kept his beehives. He had collected them over the years and now had ten or more of the white wooden 'houses' all standing in a row, like sentries among the wild flowers that grew between the bushes. He lifted the lids off of one or two of them at random to check that the inhabitants 'were doing their duty' totally undeterred by any possibility that they might sting him. If one did inadvertently attack him he felt sorry for the bee because it was likely to die.

"Oh dear, poor little devil," he would mutter, as he brushed it away like dust and carried on regardless.

"Come on you lot!" he said to them "I want lots of honey this spring, we may have cause for celebration, you get busy and do your business or out you go!"

Once he was satisfied that all was in order he continued his stroll back to the bungalow, where he hoped Alice had made him his cheese sandwich – that is, if there was any cheese left! They were only allowed to buy 4 oz per week per person.

"Not enough to keep a flea alive." he moaned.

He could eat four ounces on one sandwich before the government had rationed everything in sight! Still, there were certainly plenty of wild flowers in the field to keep the bees happy. He'd live on bread and honey if he had to – if there was any bread!

A few days after the death of Mussolini the news came on the wireless that Hitler had committed suicide in his underground bunker and the lack of cheese suddenly became very insignificant. Charles was the happiest of men.

8th May 1945 – Chippenham

The first that Joan knew that something very special had happened was when the head teacher came in and whispered something in her teacher's ear. Both ladies grabbed each other and did a little dance in front of the blackboard. The children thought it was ever so funny and everybody laughed.

"Oh my word!" cried Mrs. Paget, "We think the war is over – we *do* think that Germany has surrendered now!" She was crying and both ladies ran out of the classroom together. Suddenly, as an afterthought, Mrs. Paget ran back, totally flustered and waving her arms in the air.

"Stay there children, stay there!" she laughed and cried at the same time. "I'll be back in a minute."

They all sat in silence, not understanding what was going on at all but too amazed to make a noise or run about. The teacher came back a few minutes later having recovered her composure.

It was, indeed, true. Suddenly there was the sound of squealing from the older children in the next door classroom. Some were frightened at the sudden activity and started crying while others thought it was great fun to have something different going on.

Then the church bells started. Most of the children had never heard the sound before. They had been stopped before they were born. Everyone ran out into the playground to listen as more church bells joined in as the message spread. Some of the youngsters, many of whom were still little more than three years old clung to the skirts of any adult they could find.

'Miss' tried once again to compose herself and spoke to the children, tears streaming down her face.

"All of you – go back to your tables!" she cried "I am sure your mummies will be coming for you soon. You can go home as soon as they arrive."

Almost as soon as she had finished speaking, excited people started to arrive at the School to take their children away, as the teachers manfully tried to keep notes of who went where. Not that it mattered – very few would be back.

Joan and Ann sat and waited as their friends, one by one, were taken away by their emotional mothers. They tried to colour their pictures but there was so much going on it was hard to concentrate. Then, one of the older girls arrived with some milk and the little orange tins of Ovaltine tablets but gradually the classroom emptied, and the bells did not stop.

Every so often one of the other teachers ran in and gave Mrs. Paget a hug and then do a little dance and ran out again. The children thought it was all very odd indeed. All they did understand was that everybody seemed to be very happy all of a sudden so it stopped them from being too frightened.

Finally, Lily and Vera arrived together, both crying and laughing, and both temporarily forgetting that there was still a war going on in the Far East. It wasn't *yet* over for the head teacher who was sending the children on their way. Her husband was still out there somewhere and she didn't even know where! When it occurred to Lily she tried to show a 'bit of decorum' as she shook hands with Mrs. Williams.

"I'm sure it will be all over in the Far East too!" she said, "and your husband will be home safely!"

Mrs. Williams gave her a watery smile.

It was still early afternoon as Joan and Ann walked down the road with their mothers, but this time, instead of going back to Mrs. Stephen's house in Palmer Street, everyone seemed to be moving in the general direction of the Market Square. The whole place was packed and people were smiling and singing "Rule Britannia."

Some American soldiers drove through the streets in their Army vehicles, honking the horns and with their headlights flashing. Others picked the children up, whirling them and their mothers around in the air.

Lily and Vera thought everywhere had gone mad and they were grateful when two Canadian soldiers swung their daughters up onto their shoulders out of the way of the trampling feet of the crowds. It was like being in a dream only this time they did not want to wake up. After six years it was hard to take in and she wished so much that Stan was there with them.

Somebody turned up with an accordion, and started playing the 'Hokey Kokey', and everybody formed in a circle and did the dance together with all the children.

'Union Jacks' appeared out of nowhere, just as if their owners had been in readiness for this very special moment.

Then another person started off 'Hands, Knees and Bumps a Daisy' and the children found themselves being put down on the floor again as they 'bumped' their bottoms against the shins of the adults towering above them in their efforts to do the dance.

Above all the continuous sound of cheering and singing could be heard the relentless church bells, gradually being added to by those from neighbouring places of worship as the bell-ringers got into the buildings and dusted them down.

But there *was* still a black out. Had there not been one, it is possible that the party would have gone on and on. Lily and Vera had to get their children back to the digs, but even for those without responsibility the festivities had to end.

As dusk began to fall, so the ARP Wardens got agitated and people were encouraged to go home. The remnants of Hitler's Air Force still might have something planned and nobody wanted to take any chances.

Lily arrived back in the digs to find a telegram waiting for her from Stan saying that he would be home as soon as 'the powers-that-be' let him. She, of course, realised immediately that it would take time to get all the troops back if it were to be done in an orderly fashion. Besides, over 305,000 of them would never return – how on earth could she complain? Their lives, put on hold for the past six years could soon begin again.

Stan in Egypt 1945

Mrs. Stephens, with the help of Vera, tried to make a special dinner while Lily looked after the children, (or as special as it could be under the circumstances). She felt that she never wanted to see rabbit pie or stew ever again in her entire life, but there were fresh peas and carrots and a jelly had been found from somewhere for the pudding. She looked round the table at everyone and smiled to herself. Rationing was the best diet there was – for the adults anyway. The only ones to still look pudgy were Joan and Ann, fed on a diet of Ovaltine tablets, Vitamins and Bread and milk, they still had plenty of meat on them!

Her hosts had tried so hard and really Lily could not fault their hospitality.

Mr. Stephens put the wireless on and they listened to the music and the sound of bells ringing and the happy voices of people in the streets of London. Then they heard the gentle and slightly stuttering voice of the King.

> *"Today we give thanks to Almighty God for a great deliverance. Speaking from our Empire's oldest capital city, war battered but never for a moment daunted or dismayed – speaking from London, I ask you to join with me in that act of thanksgiving…."*

All the women wiped tears from their eyes. Bless the man!

Then there was some more music and the sound of cheering followed by the more forceful and rich vibrant voice of Winston Churchill. He tried, in vain, to calm the euphoria down, just a bit, because of the war still going on in the Far East.

> *"We may allow ourselves a brief period of limited rejoicing," he said.*

All Joan could think about was that she would be going back to Granny and Granddad and that next month she would be four and she would be able to go to the big gardens.

The following morning Lily went out to the nearest public phone box and made a telephone call to the Gabriel's. It was a terrible line, it always was, and she hated using the phone. It was something that she was not used to at all, but she heard the voice of Mrs. Gabriel on the other end and quickly pressed Button A.

"Oh Mrs. Gabriel, Madam," she said in her poshest 'telephone voice'. "Could somebody please tell my father-in-law that we will be home tomorrow?"

She heard the genuinely posh voice of Mrs. Gabriel on the other end saying something like "Oh how wonderful my dear….!" and then they were cut off.

But it was enough. She knew that 'Madam' would ensure that her gardener got the message. She was totally reliable and almost looked upon being a 'messenger' as part of her war work!

The next stop was a trip to the kindergarten to say thank you to the teachers.

There were only a few of the local children milling about and some very bleary eyed staff. Ann and Joan had made lots of friends and were sorry to be leaving them behind, but they were even sorrier that there would be no more tins of Ovaltine tablets. Vera and Lily gave Mrs. Paget a hug, and the children gave her a bunch of wild flowers they had picked on the way. They would never see her again after today.

There were suitcases to pack and a train to catch. The Mickey Mouse gas masks were left behind with Mr. Stephens and they left Palmer Street forever.

1945 – Gardener's Cottage

It was 9th May 1945 and Charles Ratcliff felt ten years younger as he walked across the meadow, which by now was full of buttercups and daisies. Just yesterday the Germans surrendered and the bells in the village rang, it seemed, forever!

He, Alice and Rosa went with Mr. and Mrs. Mumford and Edna into the village and joined in all the happy celebrations as gradually, bit by bit, the news travelled that the war, in Europe anyway, was over. What was more, they had just had a letter, that morning, from Stan, to say that he was expecting to be home within the next couple of months when his tour of duty in Egypt would finish.

The sun was shining and the birds started to sing, it seemed, louder than before. There was even a cuckoo in the distance letting everyone know that he was going to enjoy this first day of peace too. Charles went through the iron gate and crossed the top of the drive into the vegetable garden. Even the squirrels seemed to be out in force today and more daring then usual. One came right up close so that he could touch it.

"Hello, old fella!" he laughed, as the animal scampered up the oak tree. "No more bombs and doodlebugs to worry you!"

He was just about to go into the big greenhouse when he spotted Mrs. Elsie Gabriel hurrying towards him.

"Ratcliff! Ratcliff!" she shouted, "Lily and the child are on their way home today!"

Charles was getting a bit old in the tooth for somersaults but he did feel like doing one. However, he decided that it was 'all in his brain' and not his body so he changed his mind.

"Oh thank you Madam!" he cried and resisted the temptation to give her a big hug. Instead, he turned to Rosa, who was just arriving in the gardens ready for the day.

"Rosa, your sister-in-law is coming home – nip back and tell your mother!"

Life would soon get back to normal. After all, his other daughter Doris had already returned to her home. When Lily went away, Doris decided to take her young child, Roger, out of range of the V2's as well and had stayed with her in-laws until peace was declared. Now, the scattered family would soon be back together again and it would be cause for celebration.

But Charles's euphoria was tempered suddenly by caution. Millions of servicemen and civilians had died and the stories about what had happened in Hitler's Concentration camps were just trickling through. Little did he know it on that lovely day in early May, but it would be decades before people grasped the full enormity of it all and even then it would be hard to take in. Ordinary people did not, yet, really know how close we had come to total invasion.

Closer to home, Stan and Lily would have to pick up the pieces again and eventually find somewhere to live, although he had already made up his mind that they could stay in the bungalow as long as needed. It wasn't very satisfactory though – not for any young couple.

He realised that his thoughts were getting ahead of themselves. Just let's get them all home – that's the main thing! They can sort everything else out in due course.

Rosa ran across the field and found her mother out in the garden with the washing tub. She always did the washing outside in nice weather and then put it through the big mangle before hanging it up on the line to dry. Water was boiled in the big copper pot in the yard and it was, frankly, easier to simply put the tin tub on a bench and wash the clothes there. She was up to her armpits in soap suds when Rosa arrived with the news.

Alice.

"Oh thank goodness for that!" she cried, and her apron went over her face as she wiped away her tears of joy. "Oh, I must make a cake!"

The washing was forgotten and the water left to go cold. She rushed back into the kitchen and searched in her cupboard to see if she had enough ingredients. She had saved her sugar rations for this very event and had collected fresh eggs that morning. Then she hurried back outside to the well in the back garden and hoisted up the bucket containing the margarine from where it had been put to keep cool. She had saved a bit by giving Charles 'bread and scrape' on his sandwiches. The well had not been used for water for years but it was ideal as a 'larder'.

Charles had made a big heavy lid to put over it to stop the children from falling into the deep hole and to protect it from any wild-life.

Rosa helped her mother drag the lid back into place and then ran back to the gardens leaving Alice happily making her cake despite the fact that no-one would have sugar in their tea all week as a result!

It was teatime by the time the train from Chippenham arrived at Woking station and Lily was exhausted. It had been a happy journey though and there were willing hands to help with the luggage and the children. Vera had been with her as far as Guildford. The trains were heaving with cheerful people all chatting to each other as if they had known each other for years, plus hundreds of servicemen all anxious to get home to their loved ones.

At each station they could see union jacks out along the platforms and people waved anything they could get hold of. People burst into choruses of "Rule Britannia" and "God Save the King!" at the drop of a hat. Some soldiers crowded onto the train and cheerily pushed down the corridor singing "Hitler has only got one ball."

Vera and Lily went quite red.

"Oh I say!" gasped Lily.

However, everyone was happy, and that's what counted. Moreover, with all the activity the journey passed by very quickly.

Lily was relieved that they could get back to their own bed and, if she were honest, better food. Rationing was hard for everyone though. In, what seemed like no time at all it was time for Vera and Ann to leave the train and they jumped down onto the platform.

"Bye Vera!" said Lily "I do hope things go well for you – bye-bye Ann my dear!"

"Cheerio!" replied Vera, "take care."

The door slammed behind them and they were gone.

By the time they arrived at Woking Lily was glad that she had put Joan's reins on her. She had protested with fervour – she hated the things because they stopped her going where she wanted to go.

"Oh Mummy, I don't want those, I'm a big girl now!"

"Just this one last time!" Lily had said, but now she was glad she did and she was even more pleased to climb onto the bus where she was offered a seat by a very handsome sailor. She sunk into it with the child on her lap and stared out of the window as the vehicle went along the so familiar streets. She couldn't understand why she felt so exhausted.

It wasn't until the bus drew up by the stop outside the bungalow and Joan saw Charles and Alice waiting by the front gate that the child really grasped what was happening. Of course Lily had told her. Everyone had talked about 'nothing else but' since the bells had started ringing but she had not really taken it in.

Her grandparents knew the times of the buses, and Alice had gone out every half hour practically all afternoon. Now she was joined by Charles who came striding forward as he spotted his daughter-in-law being helped by the bus conductor. Lily bent down and unclipped the reins. She knew exactly which direction Joan would be running in and there would be no need for any restraint to stop her from going anywhere else! In a minute she was in her Granddad's arms, and Alice had her apron over her face yet again.

"I have just been 'vackerated' Granddad!" she told him earnestly and it all ended in laughter.

The celebrations for VE Day went on and on even though there was still, officially, a black-out, and Charles continued to attend his Home Guard. After all, there could be spies lurking and nobody was taking any chances!

However, if anybody thought that things were going to be back as they were before 1939 in an instant, they were to be bitterly disappointed. It would be years before people would recover and, if anything, the rationing got worse.

Lily was disappointed that Stan was not home straight away but she soon realised that, like many others, he had to take his turn.

"You can't expect a war to end one day and the troops to be home the next!" said Charles.

"No, I suppose not." Lily agreed, "It's just a shame that he will not be home in time for his daughter's fourth birthday though seeing as how he missed the other three."

She had to be content with his letters, many of which contained photographs of him posing in the sunshine of Egypt. It was totally the opposite of how she felt – she was tired, felt dreadful and was emotionally drained.

"He can be such a show off at times!" said Rosa as she studied the latest photo of her handsome brother

The first Joan knew that her mother was not very well was when, in the middle of the night, she was turfed out of the big bed and put in the little one in the corner.

"Just for tonight!" said Alice, "You go to sleep and we will get the Doctor to mummy in the morning".

Despite the disturbance in the night she was still 'awake with the lark' and running through to go 'out the back' on her own. Usually Lily was right behind her, but not this time.

Charles poked his head round the bedroom door and took one look at his daughter-in-law lying motionless, her face quite yellow looking.

"You look like a blasted Jap my girl!" he tried to joke, "I don't need any doctor to tell me what *you* have got – yellow jaundice – that's what you have got."

He came out to the kitchen.

"She's got jaundice Kate," he said, "I'll cycle down to the village and get Doctor Cook to her."

Joan was busy eating her porridge but she was well aware of all the activity and it was plain that her mother was not well.

"She does look very yellow!" said Alice. "Oh I do hope she is better before Stanley comes home."

Charles didn't continue the conversation. He had already put his cycle clips around the bottom of his trousers and he was off down the village.

"She needs to drink gallons of water." said Doctor Cook when he came back into the kitchen after examining the invalid. "I have just told her – she must drink at least eight pints a day to flush herself out."

Joan looked on while the doctor told Charles and Alice that Lily did, indeed, have yellow jaundice.

"Can I go and see mummy?" she said. She *really* wanted to go and see if she was yellow like Granny said.

"Just for a minute and then you must leave her in peace." said the doctor.

Doctor Cook had propped Lily up in bed on three pillows and her face was very yellow and her eyes looked sunken and dark.

She was in no mood for light hearted conversation with her daughter. All she wanted was to get better before Stan came home and she would drink the Thames dry if need be.

"Come on Joannie," said Alice, "you go and play and we will have to put your little bed in Auntie Rosa's room for a few days."

She was carrying a huge jug of water and was closely followed by Charles who was dragging the commode along the passage while the child looked on in horror. She didn't like the colour of her mummy at all.

"If you have to drink eight pints of water a day you can not go out the back all the time," said the ever practical Charles as he put the commode by Lily's bed.

She was too weak to argue but was grateful all the same. She briefly wondered what she would have done if she had been living at her mother's with the tin loo and Phyllis, Elsie and her two youngest brothers running in and out, not to mention Henry and his stinky old pipe.

At first she felt as though she couldn't lift her head from the pillow to even drink, but bit by bit, and under the strict regime of Alice, she drank her water by the pint. The angel that was Stan's mum helped her onto the commode, emptied it when it was full and then came back to make her drink some more.

For a while Doctor Cook or the district nurse came every day, but gradually the strict discipline of drinking all the water seemed to have some effect and together with the total bed-rest and the dedication of Alice, Lily started to recover and got her normal complexion back.

"Just as well," grumbled Charles, "I can't have any of *my* family looking like a ruddy Jap!"

"Charles!" cried Alice, "not in front of our granddaughter!"

Her granddaughter was only too pleased that her mummy was getting better so that she did not have to sleep in Auntie Rosa's room any more It wasn't the same as being with her mother – besides, she snored.

8. *"Ground that Hitler never got to walk on"*

Summer 1945 – Portsmouth

Stan Ratcliff tried to keep on his feet among the crowd of men all trying to be the first to see the coast of England again. If any more of them tried to push towards the front of the little minesweeper it would surely turn turtle!

It had been a long and tiring journey from Egypt to Palestine and then along the North African coast. The men slept on tables in the canteen and on any spare piece of floor there was, along with the crew, and all with one aim in common – to get back home as quickly as possible by whatever method! He had written to the folks and to Lily but they didn't know exactly when to expect him, any more than he did. All he could do was phone Mr. Gabriel when the ship arrived at Portsmouth. It was already three months since VE day and the mail had been all over the place.

"Now, there's a situation!" he thought to himself, "I bet the queue for the phones will be a mile long – I could simply get on the train and get home quicker than it would take to let them know."

The ship was rocking about and it was all he could do to stay upright, but it was a mix of adrenalin and euphoria that was keeping everyone going. Nervousness too – most of the men had not seen their loved ones for years and didn't know what they would find when they got home.

"You OK Flight?"

He couldn't complain about his promotion. He had arrived in Malta a corporal and left as a sergeant, and now on leaving Egypt he was a flight sergeant.

He turned round and saw the familiar face of his second in command from the MT Section, corporal 'Chalky White'.

"God Almighty, I'll be glad to get off this boat won't you Flight?" he growled, "even having a pee is a major operation – damn it, I've just been over the side – it's not exactly the latest in luxury is it?"

Stan laughed, "Well at least we are in one piece Corporal – I feel as though I have used up all of my nine lives a hundred times over and, frankly, I couldn't care less if it was a tin bath!"

The pushing and shoving carried on as the ship waited to dock, amongst dozens of others of various shapes and sizes. A brass band was playing on the quayside and people were waving union jacks. It was just one great wall of sound and many of the men had tear-stained faces. Most of them had been sea-sick, but the awful journey was forgotten in the elation of being home. The friends hung onto their kit-bags and waited patiently as the minesweeper docked.

"Keep well Chalky!" Stan patted him on the back, "Who knows, maybe our paths will cross again."

The two men hugged each other and then Stan turned round to thank some of the crew. They had put up with so much on the journey back. All would have tales to tell and all had mixed feelings ranging between hysteria, elation, sadness and the horrors of war.

He could now see why his father never spoke about the First World War. It wasn't the sort of thing you *could* speak about. It was like the old man had said, – "You could speak about the going and you could speak about the coming back – it was the 'bit in between' that you would rather draw a veil over."

The only thing any of the blokes had on their mind just at this moment in time was to get home and Stan had already missed his daughter's fourth birthday by a long way.

He felt in his uniform pocket and pulled out a screwed up photo of Lily with Joan taken in Chippenham. His wife looked as beautiful as ever, with her slim figure and dark curls and the youngster was no longer a baby, but a little girl.

A wave of bitterness swept over him at missing out on most of his child's babyhood, followed almost immediately by guilt. There were so many around him straining for a glimpse of a loved one, or rushing for the first train to where they were. At least his journey was almost over.

Stan was pushed along with the flow of humanity, and he slung his kitbag onto his shoulder. His feet were on English soil and for many of the younger men the emotion became too much. It was all over – for most of them so was life in the military and there would be a lot of adjusting to do. He felt like kissing the ground and many around him did. It was ground that Hitler never got to walk on after all, though he came mighty close.

Summer 1945 – Gardener's Cottage

"Lily! Lily!" it was Edna from over the road. She was breathless with running. "There has been a phone call up at the house. Stan's ship has arrived at Portsmouth."

Edna almost fell on top of her friend as she rushed to the door.

Lily had fully recovered from the yellow jaundice. It had taken three weeks and Alice had been at her side constantly.

In some ways it was divine providence that Stan was delayed in Egypt. She would not have wanted him to come home and find her in the condition she had been throughout most of June and July. Joan was just glad that her mummy did not 'look like a jap' – not that she knew what a jap was.

"The Gabriel's had a phone call!" Edna went on. "He's here – he's come on a minesweeper!!"

"Oh my word!" Lily felt herself running around in circles for a minute and then composed herself.

"I'm going to meet him!" she cried, quickly searching for her purse and coat, "Oh bum – I haven't even had my hair in curlers today."

Joan was helping her Granddad to eat his elevenses at the kitchen table.

"How old are you young lady?" said Charles suddenly out of the blue.

"You *know* how old I am Granddad, I am four!" she replied in disgust.

"Did I, or did I not promise that I would take you to the gardens when you are four?"

She jumped down from the table and he was spared from losing any more of his cheese.

"You mean the real gardens Granddad? The real gardens where the bloomin eye-tyes are!?"

Everyone rolled around laughing except for Edna, who looked puzzled, and Lily, who already had brushed her hair whilst still wishing that she had put it in curlers.

"Go-on!" he grinned "go and find your dungarees!"

"Oh Dad!" exclaimed Lily, "You can't let Stan see his daughter, after all this time, wearing your cut down trousers."

"Do you really think he is going to worry about what she is wearing Lil'?" he retorted, "Go on with you now, or you will miss the bus – don't worry, I'll keep her clean – you go and bring my son home!"

Lily did not trust him to keep her clean for one minute, but she urgently needed to get a move on and there was no further argument. She quickly tied a bow in her daughter's hair but she was under no illusions – she would probably come back without it anyway.

Then the girls went off together, Lily in the direction of the bus stop, and Edna and Rosa back to work.

Alice started burrowing through the larder to see what rations she had got so that she could put on a nice tea when her son got home and a belated birthday party for her granddaughter and little grandson Roger. What with all the activity and Lily becoming ill their birthdays had all but been overlooked.

There was a tin of corned beef and there was salad growing in the garden. She ran around like someone demented, occasionally stopping to wipe her eyes on her apron.

"Look Granddad, I'm ready for the garden!" cried Joan, as she emerged from the bedroom wearing her favourite dungarees which were now getting very short in the leg.

Charles brushed down the wheelbarrow for her to sit in.

"Come on Madam!" he replied in his poshest of voices, "your chariot awaits you!"

She did not need telling twice! For the very first time she was going to go through the mysterious iron gate at the top of the meadow.

"And when we come home for tea!" said Charles, "Your father will be here!"

She couldn't have cared less. All she wanted to do was to have an adventure and see the gardens.

She climbed into the wheelbarrow. This, to her, was what life was all about. It had been lots of fun to go to the school and to make friends with other children but she was four now and could go to the gardens and possibly pick strawberries. She felt very important indeed.

Charles carefully closed the gate behind him and wheeled his granddaughter through to the herb garden, and to what was the back of Coxhill Manor. She marvelled at the size of the place and its huge amount of windows. You could fit Granddad's little bungalow into it twenty times over.

There was also a big goldfish pond with a wall around it and he lifted her up and held her tight while she stood on the edge and looked down at the bright orange fish. It was the first time she had ever seen real fish swimming about and her days of 'being semi-evacuated' were already paling into insignificance.

She could have stood there on the wall and watched for hours but Charles' arm was getting tired and he spotted Mrs. Gabriel coming out of the house with her bulldog, George, on his lead. He lifted the child down and waited for his employer to stroll over.

"Hello Ratcliff!" said Mrs. Gabriel "such wonderful news about your son isn't it? Hello Joannie my dear!"

Joan held on to her Granddad's big strong hand as Mrs. Gabriel sat down on the wall to rest her legs.

She was quite a striking woman, tall and slim with a very straight back, and good posture, although she was well into her seventies. She wore a long cotton dress and a wide brimmed hat, to shield her from the August sunshine, plonked on her grey curls. George sat meekly at her side not in the least bit bothered at this interruption to his walk.

"So lovely that your daddy is coming back at last Joannie!" she went on.

George looked on patiently as they all spoke together. He was a handsome dog, the quintessential British bulldog, and although he looked tough he would not harm a fly.

"Go on you can stroke his head!" said Mrs. Gabriel generously, "he won't hurt you."

She did so gingerly, and then she caught sight of a frog jumping around the water-lilies.

"Oh look, a frog, – if you hold a frog upside-down his eyes pop out!" she seriously informed the two adults.

Charles almost exploded with laughter! Where did she get it from?

"Is that so?" smiled his employer sweetly, "Well I never knew that!"

"Oh yes, one of the big girls told me at my school.!"

"Well!" said the old lady kindly, "There's a thing – we had best leave him to run away then because we don't want his eyes popping out on us do we?"

"Granddad is going to show me the diddy-dottems!"

'Diddy-dottems' was her word for grapes. Nobody really knew where she got it from but everyone guessed that the culprit was standing right beside her and nobody ever tried to correct it.

"And the bloomin' eye-tyes as well," she explained excitedly.

Mrs. Gabriel felt that she was singularly lacking in her knowledge of the language of four year olds.

Charles bid farewell to a very puzzled lady and George before his granddaughter could 'drop him in it further'.

The grapes were just ripening and she looked up at the huge glass structure with the vine growing all over its roof and the fruits hanging from it in big black bunches. There were scores of them and most would be used for making wine. Just for once she was speechless.

He climbed up the ladder and cut some down to take into the kitchen of the big house and another bunch to take home.

"If you eat too many of those they will give you a belly-ache because they are not quite ripe yet," he said as he stretched up to tie some loose ones in.

He climbed down and picked off one or two and then carefully closed the greenhouse door as he led her outside and along the path to the strawberry patch.

"These are riper," he said. "You can pick some and put them in the bowl but don't eat too many or I will have your mother after me." He took a large tin bowl from out of the wheelbarrow.

"You go along the rows where the straw is – don't tread on the plants – and fill this."

She was in her element and Charles had completely forgotten about his promise to Lily to keep her clean and nobody worried that the fruit hadn't been washed.

"Oh get away – it will spoil the flavour!" Charles had grunted, when Lily had last mentioned it, "You've got to eat a bit of dirt before you die!"

Joan bit into one and the red juice was instantly all over her face and down the front of her dungarees.

"Watch out for pesky slugs!" said Charles, "You don't want to end up eating one of those."

She knew just exactly what 'pesky slugs' were. Her Granddad had them in his own garden and sometimes he put salt on them. 'Pesky slugs' did not like salt. It made them turn 'inside-out'!

By the time she had filled the bowl most of the juice was down her front.

"Oh blimey!" said Charles, suddenly remembering, "Your mother is not going to be very pleased with me Joannie, come on let's try and clean you up."

He put her bowl in his barrow and then led her into the big kitchen where Cook lifted her up onto the big draining board and did a very good job of wiping her face and hands. There was, however, nothing that could be done about the stains on the dungarees.

"Oh well," said Charles, "I don't think my son will care!"

"You dirty little pup!" laughed Cook as she lifted her down.

"That's what mummy says." Joan informed her, then as an afterthought.

"Granddad, I haven't seen the bloomin eye-tyes yet!"

"Oh they have gone!" said Cook quickly coming to the rescue, "they've gone back to Eye-tye Land."

"Where's Eye-tye Land?"

"Oh far, far, away!" said Cook, "over the sea."

"Not far enough away!" mumbled Charles under his breath.

The conversation was suddenly ended by the arrival of Rosa who whispered excitedly in her father's ear.

"Stanley's home!" she said.

"Come on young lady!" said Charles trying hard to contain himself, "It's time to go, – let's leave the diddy-dottems for Mr. and Mrs. Gabriel."

Cook went over to the larder and came back with a tin of ham.

"Here," she said, "You give this to your Granny to open for tea."

"Oooh thank you!"

"Thank you!" said Charles, "Thank you Cook – say goodbye Joannie."

With that he took the tin off his granddaughter in case she dropped it and together they strode over to where he had left the wheelbarrow and she climbed in.

"Whee – off we go!" he cried, and pushed her towards the entrance to the meadow. The squirrels were in their usual tree by the gate almost like a guard of honour waiting for him.

"Hello Sammy and Sally!" cried Charles, naming them on the spot, "my boy is home you know!"

The squirrel's tails had never been bushier, the meadow had never been greener and the buttercups and daisies never more profuse than on that day towards the end of August 1945.

"Hold tight Joannie!" he cried, knowing that the minute he closed the gate, Alice would spot him, and they would all come out of the house.

He saw Alice first, coming out of the back door towards the field. Then behind her, framed by the doorway, was Lily with the tall bronzed figure of his only son with his arm around her waist.

"Look, look who's over there!" said Charles pushing the barrow even faster. He felt a wave of pride come over him.

Joan watched as her mother and Granny stood to one side and a handsome dark haired man brushed past them and moved forward towards the gate, an imposing figure in his Royal Air Force uniform. She felt she vaguely recognised him. He didn't run, but just walked with long steady strides towards them.

Charles stopped and allowed Joannie to jump out and in a minute the man had stooped down to her level. She could see he looked like the person in the latest photograph by the side of her bed and the smile and twinkling eyes were also familiar to her.

"I saw you when we were 'vackerated" she said knowledgeably.

"You certainly did," he replied.

She politely gave him a kiss on the cheek before running across the last few yards of meadow to where Lily and Alice were waiting. She had more important things on her mind but if Stan was disappointed he didn't show it. It was to be expected.

"I saw the 'diddy-dottems'" she told everyone, "and I picked strawberries."

Father and son hugged each other. There was nothing to say.

They followed the ladies into the bungalow where Joannie was already doing enough chattering to make up for everyone!

"I saw frogs in the pond'!" she was saying when Charles and Stan arrived indoors, "but" she added with a very serious face, "I didn't see any bloomin eye-tyes, because they have all gone back to Eye-tye Land which is far far away."

"And that's where they can bloomin' well stay!" grunted Charles as he took off his trilby hat and hung it on the peg.

"Language Charles!" said Alice, out of habit.

Joan ran back outside and picked up the bowl of strawberries from the wheelbarrow and held it up for her grandmother. They looked a bit squashed but nobody minded.

"Look what I picked!"

"We'll have those for tea with some 'hundreds and thousands on!" said Alice. She'd used all the sugar ration on the cake! The child ran back outside again and picked up the tin of ham.

This was a luxury. Alice put it carefully in the larder. Doris, Harry and Roger were coming over tomorrow and the ham would come in very handy for a very special celebration she was planning.

Quite suddenly, Charles leant over and helped himself to a piece of celery that Lily had been preparing for tea. He popped it in his mouth like a cigar and put his grey trilby back on his head but cocked to one side.

"I now think we can allow ourselves a short period of rejoicing!" he said, mimicking his idol – Winston Churchill.

Everyone dissolved into peals of laughter as Alice laid the cups and saucers out on the table. Nobody noticed, or cared, that Stan's daughter was in her dungarees and they were covered in strawberry juice and other muck from the wheelbarrow. Lily looked radiant.

"You know Mum," sighed Stan, with a great deal of feeling, "that is the nicest cup of tea I have ever had – ever!"

Later, after tea, Joannie sat on her grandfather's lap and chatted to the man that had come into her life again and looked at him 'from a distance'.

"I can't believe how she has grown up!" Stan said, when they had all settled down for the evening.

He had missed out on so much, but he was quite happy to let her 'hold court' from her Granddad's knee by the fireplace It was poetic justice really.

He could just remember his dad going off to the First World War when he had been four. Rosa was six, while his younger sister, Doris, had been eighteen months old. It was only now that he was starting to realise how dreadful it must have been Like Joan he had not understood at the time, and Charles had been like a stranger coming back into the house after the years away. No, he did not begrudge the old man a single second. His own time would come.

Lily too was content to just sit in the armchair with her husband sitting on the arm at her side. They could talk about the future during the next few days. She also had to remind herself that he wasn't home for good just yet. He still had to report back to the Dispersal Centre in Staffordshire but at least there was no chance of him being sent abroad again – demob was only weeks away.

It hardly seemed possible and if it was a dream – then she did not want to wake up.

Stan caught sight of the rainbow picture propped up on the mantelpiece and leaned forward to pick it up.

"I see Granddad still has this?" he said.

"That is Granddad's very own rainbow isn't it Granddad!" his daughter informed him "a rainbow is when God says that everything is going to be all right!" Then as an afterthought, as if to verify her statement, "Granddad said so didn't you Granddad?"

He resisted reminding her that he had been there when she had painted it!

"It is the most beautiful rainbow I have ever seen!" said Stan.

"I saw a real one when we were 'vackerated and I went to school!" she informed him, and then as if for confirmation, "didn't I Mummy?"

"Yes you did."

Lily didn't bother explaining that it wasn't really a proper evacuation – not like the older boys and girls.

"and....we did 'Hands, knees and bumps a daisy, and..." she went on, "we had nice tasting tablets in a tin didn't we Mummy?"

"Yes you did!" she laughed.

"And I had a Mickey Mouse head to put on with big ears – didn't I Mummy?"

Lily felt that if she let her daughter go on much longer they would be there all night.

"Come on, young lady, that's enough excitement for one day."

"Well Kate!" said Charles to Alice as he looked at the clock, "I think it is time I went off to do my duty!" He lifted Joan to the floor as Alice put a bowl of bread and milk on the table. The routine still had not altered.

The Home Guard were still meeting in the village but more out of habit than necessity.

"Tell your father what this is called?" said Charles as he came back carrying his tin hat.

"A Gazunder Granddad!" she said patiently, "everybody knows that!"

"And why is it called a Gazunder?" said Charles.

"Because it gazunder the bed." she humoured him.

"Well, come on then child," he suddenly said, "what are you waiting for – go and put it there then – go on with you."

He handed her the tin hat and everyone giggled as she followed him into the main bedroom and placed it under her grandparent's bed alongside the chamber pot.

"Don't go using it in the night by mistake!" said Stan.

"Listen son." replied Charles, "If I use it in the night I can promise you that it will *not* be a mistake."

Everybody roared with laughter as he went out of the back door to his bike and rode off down the village singing 'Rule Britannia' at the top of his voice and with the lamplight shining on the front even though it was not yet dark – but just because he could.

"He has gone looking for pies again," Joan informed them as Lily carted her off to get ready for bed.

Stan followed Lily and his daughter into the bedroom at a discreet distance and stood back and watched while she said her prayers.

"God bless mummy and daddy, and Granny and Granddad and my other Granny and Granddad and my aunties and uncles." She jumped up and went to kiss the photo of her father.

"Oi, oi," called Lily, "he's here, look!"

Joan looked up and saw the same kindly face. It was a bit thicker set and the hair was going grey but she could see the likeness. It was hard to understand but she ran up to him and kissed his cheek dutifully. Then she knelt down on the floor beside the bed again.

"And thank you God for bringing my daddy home safely."

Both Lily and Stan brushed their eyes.

Lily didn't bother pulling the curtains together. There was no more blackout. Joan had lost her place in the big bed though and had to go in the little one in the corner again but she didn't mind too much. It wasn't as bad as the recess at Chippenham or Auntie Rosa's.

It was all right for the moment, but everyone realised that thought would have to be given to finding a home.

"Night night, see you in the morning," said Lily as she tucked her in.

"I'm going to school again soon, aren't I Mummy?".

"You certainly are!" said Lily, "Go to sleep now!"

Stan stood at the foot of the bed and watched his wife and daughter. He came up and kissed the child on the cheek as Lily moved away. How many days had he waited for this moment? She politely put her arms around his neck and informed him that she was four now and would be going to school soon.

"I know!" he smiled "Goodnight – sleep well!"

"Will you be here tomorrow?" she said.

"I certainly will." Stan replied.

"Goodnight!" she said politely.

"See what you have been missing!" giggled Lily under her breath as she closed the door behind them.

"Cups and saucers, plates and dishes,
here comes the girl with the calico britches!"

Roger, who was just three, was doing his 'party piece'. The whole family were together to welcome the men back home and as belated birthdays for the two children. Alice, despite the rationing, had done them proud.

"Oh very good Roger!" she laughed as she lifted him down from the chair, "What a clever boy you are, – now you Joannie, your turn!"

She needed no second telling and the youngster climbed up on the chair ready to recite. The only trouble was that when she got started there was no stopping her. There was 'Baa Baa Black Sheep', 'Mary had a Little Lamb' and many others before Lily called 'time'!

"Come on, you can't do them all, give your cousin another go!"

The younger child only knew 'Cups and saucers, plates and dishes', so he recited that all over again so many times that everyone became happy to hear Joan sing 'Away in a Manger' even though it was August.

It had been a joyful day though, made all the more special because Doris and Harry did not have to worry any more about getting home before it got dark and no-one was concerned about pulling the curtains to keep the light in any more.

"Well, whose turn is it for a party piece now!" said Alice.

Suddenly Charles got to his feet and disappeared in the direction of the bedroom whilst everyone looked on puzzled.

"Now where is *he* off to?" muttered Doris, "I think Granddad is trying to get out of singing us a song children!"

However, in a few minutes he was back carrying an accordion. Everyone was dumbfounded, even Alice, for a minute.

"My goodness, you *are* honoured," she said, "he has not played that since before the First World War, I had forgotten he had got it – where did you dig that out from dear?"

"Ah ha, you would be surprised what I have got tucked away at the back of the cupboard," he grunted.

Only Rosa, apart from her mother, could just remember how her father used to entertain them 'before the first lot' and the memories came flooding back.

The instrument had been played constantly by Charles's parents and was a relic from the days when his family had all belonged to the Salvation Army in the last century. The Great

War had a very profound effect on Charles. He had come back both mentally and physically scarred, with his deep-rooted Christian beliefs sorely tested after the things he had seen on the Somme.

There were very few pictures or film of what had taken place but *he* would have pictures in his head for ever – they would never go away. From that moment on he had steadfastly left the accordion in its box and everyone had either forgotten about it or never knew of its existence in the first place.

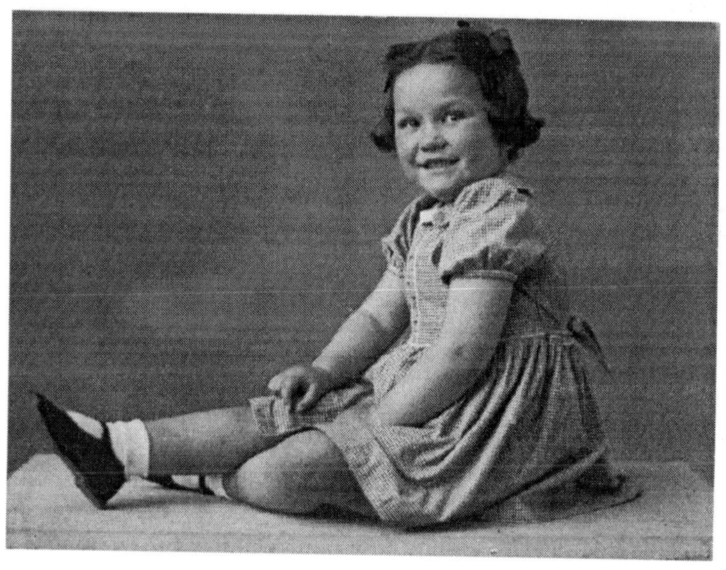

Joannie – aged four and a bit.

"I don't know if I can remember how to play it after all these years", he muttered as he got himself into position. "Now let's see what I can do."

After a few rusty notes and some stopping and starting, and the occasional curse, the talent all came flooding back to him though. He began by playing stirring 'Salvationist' music such as "What a friend we have in Jesus," but soon followed it up, with, quite bizarrely, cockney songs like "Down at the Old Bull and Bush" and "Daisy, Daisy, give me your answer do."

"Well, I'll be blessed!" laughed Stan, "You learn something new every day don't you?"

"I never knew you could play a squeezebox Dad!" laughed Doris.

"Ah you would be surprised my girl!" he grinned, "I have many hidden talents."

Rosa felt a wave of nostalgia for the time when *she* had been a child and Doris and Stan were babies. She could remember how happy and carefree everyone had been when her parents were young and then he too had gone away quite suddenly and they had never heard the 'squeezebox' again – until now. She hadn't understood why he went at the time and she remembered standing by the gate looking for him day after day until eventually giving up hope and not looking any more.

There had been countless times when she had glimpsed someone in khaki army uniform and had run towards them only to be bitterly disappointed when she found the person to be a complete stranger on his way to his own home, so she gave up her vigil. Then she was taken to visit him at a hospital down in East Sussex , near where they used to live, and there were men who had been badly burned or had limbs missing. Even now she could remember how awful it was.

For a minute Alice couldn't bear to be reminded of that time and she went out to the back door, quietly wiping away her tears. It was a very emotional for everyone and the memories were raw. Yet it was a delight to see her gruff old husband so carefree again and her children re-united at last. It was all she could do to stop bursting into floods of tears of sheer emotion and relief. She looked up into the clear June night which was free of searchlights and aeroplanes overhead and said her own little prayer. It was a prayer that was being said daily throughout the land!

"Please, *please* God, please do not let it happen again."

Then she put the latch on the door and returned to the family. She had lost a brother in 'the first lot', but her immediate family had come through it this time and she had to be grateful for that. If she had lost her son she did not know what she would have done. Her eyes filled up again at the very thought and she gave herself a little mental shake.

"Come on Kate," called Charles, "come and sing your song – you do it better than me.!"

He tinkered around with the squeezebox and some familiar notes came out that most people in the room recognised. Alice pulled herself together and went over and stood by him and, for her, Charles, Rosa and Doris, the years rolled away as she began her song in her clear soprano voice. Everyone gradually joined in with her.

> *"Count your blessings one by one,*
> *when dawn appears and day has just begun,*
> *and then you'll find they'll come again to you*
> *if you will count your blessings each day through!"*

It was the end of a perfect day and the beginning of a new future for everyone.

9. *"Suddenly she was calling him Daddy..."*

The euphoria of VE day and the relief felt in June 1945 were short-lived as people realised that rationing would get, if anything, worse, and that the war in the Far East was not yet over. Stan still had to complete his service in the RAF and was instructed to report to the dispersal centre at Hednesford in Staffordshire.

But there was a bonus – at last he was able to resurrect his motor-cycle. It was like being re-united with an old friend when he 'got his wheels' again. He had bought the bike when he had come out of the Air Force for the first time in 1935 but it had reluctantly been put away at the back of the shed in 1939 and had rarely been seen since. Charles, at least, was very glad to see it out of the way at last, if only for a while.

"Damn contraption, cluttering up the place," he would say, although there was plenty of room really. It *was* a big shed.

It soon became clear that things were not going to change any time soon though. There was going to be no 'instant housing' for everyone, and it would take decades for all the bombed buildings to be cleared and re-built, never mind the roads so that building materials could be transported. It was quite a depressing prospect.

Stan also had to turn his mind to what he was going to do when he was demobbed. He knew he had the offer of a job by Mr. Gabriel but he had hoped to go into the police force. However, he was mortified to find that, at five foot eleven inches, he was one inch too short!

"Just one bloomin' inch!" he said to the RAF Physical Training Instructor, "Can't you stretch me?"

Not that he minded working for Gabriel's. There would always be plenty of work so it was not the end of the world, but he had just fancied himself as a policeman. It was disappointing to say the least.

Joan started at the kindergarten that autumn. She hadn't been four for very long, but nevertheless off she went to the school in the village each morning feeling as though she was quite an old hand at such things.

Lily was just glad to get her little job back at Sainsbury's so it was usually Alice that took her granddaughter to school. She was able to combine this chore with a visit to the cemetery to see little Edie's 'garden' or a trip to Benham's shop to get her groceries. It was another little step towards normality.

It was fortunate for all concerned that Alice had some patience though. Like most children, Joan thought it was great to kick the leaves that were piling up on the ground with each gust of wind and to collect the shiny conkers. The trouble was that her grandmother joined in and always lost track of time!

"Oh my goodness Joannie, we are going to be late, we shall have to run now."

Alice could not have run fast to save her life but she pretended to and together they trotted down the road hand in hand and usually arrived at the school laughing and breathless.

It was quite usual for Lily to get home from work and find that Joan's top coat had conkers stuffed in the pockets but she couldn't be cross with her mother-in-law for long.

"Well they looked so nice and shiny!" said Alice, "We couldn't leave them behind could we Joannie?"

Lily raised her eyes to the heavens and gave a 'speaking' look to her daughter but said nothing – it was a small price to pay.

Most of the children at the little Infant's School in the village had been evacuated at some time or another. Every day there was a new face as they started to come back after, in some cases, years away. Consequently, nobody worried too much about how old they were or how many there were to a class. Joan also very soon learned that she was very lucky to have a daddy at all!

Some of the infants had no parents. These were the ones whose daddy's had not come back and their mothers had stayed in London while they were evacuated only to be bombed out. It was very sad. Nobody wanted to go in an orphanage so they had come to the village to be looked after by relatives

There was also a lot of talk in the playground about 'nasties'. Joan didn't know what 'nasties' were, but there were some children in her class that had 'escaped them'. These children were staying with the Reverend Asquith and they could not speak English at all. Her new friend called Pauline seemed to know everything though.

"Oh those children escaped the nasties," said Pauline, "I know all about them because my mummy told me – the nasties worked for Mr. Hitler, but he is dead now and so are the nasties."

However, that was about the sum total of Pauline's knowledge and so Joan got fed up with trying to find out any more about the nasties and contented herself with playing hop-scotch with the new children. You didn't have to speak for that!

It wasn't long before she slipped into the routine of getting to and from school.

Occasionally Granddad would turn up at the gates. Among his gardening duties was also the care of the Gabriel family grave situated in the same cemetery as Edie's just next door to the school. He would tend the plots and. afterwards, come and wait at the school gates. Then there was always a small detour to show Joannie 'what Edie's garden was looking like today'. A wooden cross, hand crafted lovingly by Charles himself, marked the spot.

"It's Edie's garden," he told her, as he freshened the water in the flowers that Alice had last put there, and made sure that there were no weeds anywhere near.

The small oak cross had an inner circle around which was written "*Suffer the little children to come unto me*" in white.

There was a bar going across the middle saying *Edith Joan Ratcliff.*

"I can read that!" she said, showing off as usual. "That's my name – Edie has got my name."

"No my dear" replied Charles quietly. "*You* have got Edie's name."

Once they were both satisfied that everything was in order the pair would stride off home to Coxhill – well, at least, Charles did the striding because, usually by this time he had his granddaughter on his back.

Then one day, just when she was beginning to think he had gone for good again, her father arrived on his motorbike. She heard him switch the engine off and then watched him wheel it down the path with mixed feelings. On the one hand she had been starting to get to know who he was, but on the other hand his visits were few and far between and when he was home he seemed to take up a lot of her mother and grandparent's time. However, he was very nice to her so she took the disruption in her stride.

It was hard to understand though. She had no concept of 'abroad' or the war beyond that which had gone on around her since she could remember. All she knew was that he had been a face in a picture and now he was real and turned up occasionally to visit. Moreover Granddad had stopped going off to look for pies and didn't cover the light on his bike any more.

She certainly enjoyed Stan's trips home though because he played games with her and did drawing and sometimes brought sweets with him. Already he was discovering that she *could* be bought! There were other times though when he became engrossed in conversations that she was not part of and then he was gone again on his motor bike and it was back to the normal routine once more.

The evacuation to Newcastle and Wiltshire were becoming just faint echoes in her young mind – a temporary disruption to what she knew as normal. The war, however, would live with the grownups forever.

"Oooh! What's this?" exclaimed Lily one morning. She picked up a letter from the mat with unfamiliar writing and stamps on it. It was addressed to Stan and was postmarked Paris.

"Who does *he* know in Paris?" she questioned.

"Maybe those French girls he stayed with!" said Rosa.

Lily put it to one side but could hardly contain her curiosity until he arrived home for the weekend and was able to open it for himself.

"Ah now, wouldn't you like to know who it is from?" he teased, when he could see how inquisitive everyone was.

"Oh come on Stanley!" said Alice, "You can't blame us for being nosy."

He opened the letter up and started to read the contents. It turned out that, indeed, it was from one of the two teenagers that he had helped to escape from occupied France back in 1940.

"It's from Genevieve – they survived the occupation and have settled in Paris!"

"Huh Genevieve eh!" chided Lily, "It's from one of his French girlfriends Mum – Rosa was right."

Stan totally ignored their taunting as he read the letter carefully. It was all written in perfect English by someone with a very neat hand. Both the girls and their mother had returned to Paris once it had been liberated and they were training to become school teachers. Needless to say they were filled with gratitude. It had taken some while to write because they had been looking for somebody to translate their letter into English as they knew that Stan did not speak their language.

"Oh this is great news!" said Stan as he passed it to Lily. He really had nothing to hide but he did enjoy teasing her at times and he was thrilled that they were O.K. It had taken four years to find out and he was delighted.

She read the letter proudly. She could see how indebted they were to him – that was obvious, and they had asked after her and the child.

"One day we will meet again" Genevieve said.

"Oh will you now?" giggled Lily, "We'll see about that!"

Joan sat at the kitchen table watching the grown-ups laughing with her daddy about 'French girlfriends'.

"You take no notice!" said Stan, "They are just jealous." It went right over her head.

The women in Stan's life would always mildly pull his leg about his 'French girlfriends' but he could cope. Despite Hitler's best efforts life was picking up again – very slowly.

1945 – Hyde Cottage

Lily never knew which brother or sister was going to be at home when she went on a visit to her parents, but she couldn't help but think that between her husband's family and her own, they had certainly paid *their* 'twopenceworth' in for King and Country, especially as both Fred and Frank were in the Military and Bob would be before long!

As for young Phyllis, she usually got the unenviable job of escorting her father back from the Sergeants Mess after an evenings drinking and cavorting. She didn't really mind though because the barracks were also home to hundreds of Canadian soldiers!

It was inevitable that she would find that extra special one. His name was Albert and she was destined to become a war bride from the moment she met him. Lily thought how ironical it was that just as Stan's family were all coming back together again *her* family were scattering across the world!

Joan was now old enough to go and play in the field at the back of the old homestead and occasionally she would spot Henry coming down the lane and run off to meet him. However, this was not quite with the same enthusiasm as with Granddad Ratcliff because, of course, Henry did not have a wheelbarrow or 'diddy-dottems' hidden in his apron!

However, what he did have was a big box which played music when you wound it up at the side.

"Come on Granddad, come and play me your music."

"All' right, just let me get in the house!" he puffed – the lane always made him out of breath – "Let me take my hat off and have a sit down at least child."

For all his old fashioned ideas, he did care about his first grandchild and, as well as playing tunes on his old wind up gramophone, he patiently told her stories about his seafaring father who travelled the world in a sailing ship. The stories were awesome to a child who had yet to see the seaside. Then there were tales about her great grandmother Charlotte who, when she was only a young woman, had been all the way from London to New Zealand in a big sailing ship all by herself and worked as a cook. Henry told how his parents had met in that far off place across the oceans and got married there.

Joan didn't really know where New Zealand was but he persevered and showed her on the globe and it did look like a very long way off indeed – certainly much further than Newcastle or Chippenham! Granddad told her that it took six months to travel all that way, tossing about on the high seas.

She wasn't sure what six months was either but knew it was a long time. As to the high seas – they were very hard to understand – high seas, low seas – they were all the same to her. Despite having fathered eight children Henry had little idea of how much a young child should be expected to understand.

"They had to come back in the end though" said Henry, ignoring her blank look, "because my father, your great Granddad, became blind. He couldn't see and there was nowhere to try and make him better in that primitive place across the other side of the world."

He was certainly a man with plenty of tales to tell but it was all such a long, long time ago and not as good as 'fireside stories' or ones about Sammy Squirrel.

"So you see" he went on – almost talking to himself by now, "how things turn out – if my father had not gone blind I would have been born in New Zealand and then I would not have met your grandma and so your mother would not be here and neither would you."

Now he had totally lost her – it was all much too complicated and the very idea of her mother 'not being here' could not be imagined at all.

She thought it was time to go and see if Granny had any biscuits. She jumped up and left him, lost in his own thoughts as he settled down to his pipe and brass band music in his smoky 'glory-hole'

One thing that she was starting to take a real dislike to, though, was the old tin toilet out at the back. Of course Granny always tried to keep it as clean and fresh as she could and the place stunk of Jeyes Fluid but everywhere else she had been had proper toilets with a chain to pull.

"Why haven't they got a toilet like my other Granny?" Joan said suddenly when they had said their goodbyes and were sitting on the bus on the way back home.

"Oh, I don't know, replied Lily "I think it is because there are no pipes going down the lane."

"Well why don't they get some pipes?"

"Oh, I expect they will one day!" she said, although she knew perfectly well that Henry would not change now, although she could never understand why. Even her sailor grandfather, way back at the turn of the century, had proper plumbing.

Once again she mentally 'took her hat off' to Grace for putting up with it and for bringing up eight children in the old place almost single handed! It had been a hard life for her – probably harder than the generation before her. However, despite the life she had lead, there were no lines on Grace's face, her eyes sparkled and her hair was always clean and shiny.

She actually did seem to be resigned to her 'lot' as she sat by the kitchen range in her flowered wrap around overall, never losing her sense of humour and taking everything in her stride.

Lily found herself thinking that her mother could do with a few of Joan's rainbows on *her* mantelpiece!

All she wanted now was for Stan to come out of the Air Force once and for all so that they could have a proper family life together and some degree of normality. He had done his bit having been in the RAF twice and she knew he would miss it but she couldn't wait for the day when he would put his uniform away for good. One thing was definite though – *she* would certainly *not* have a tin toilet anywhere in sight – not if she had anything to do with it anyway!

Autumn 1945 –RAF Dispersal Centre

Demob seemed to come upon Stan all of a sudden. One minute he was 'kicking-around' at the dispersal centre and it was taking forever, and then the next minute his Release Book had arrived and he had to go and be fitted out with 'demob' clothes.

He went round the camp 'clearing' from the different sections, including the MT Section, the Gym and the Sergeants' Mess, all the time wrestling with his thoughts and trying to decide if he was doing the right thing. Last on his list of places to visit was Stores to exchange his uniform for civilian clothes.

Stan watched his uniform jackets disappearing over the counter and got a last glimpse of his flight sergeant badges on the sleeves. Was he really being a total 'twerp'?

He was already paid as a flight sergeant and would undoubtedly be made a substantive warrant officer in no time if he signed on. It was the best rank in the Air Force – viewed with respect by the commissioned officers and looked up to by the non-commissioned.

"Are you sure about this Flight?" said the Stores Corporal as he slung Stan's uniform along the counter and pointed in the direction of the rows of civilian clothes all hanging on rails behind him. "Do you think any of this stuff will suit you?"

For a brief moment Stan hesitated – after all, the war *was* over now – in Europe anyway – and he would be entitled to a married quarter. Their housing problem would be resolved in a minute. However, he knew Lily wanted him to come out – she had made that crystal clear, and who could blame her after the past six years? Also, knowing his luck he could be sent off to Japan if he signed on – it wasn't finished there *yet*!

"Is anybody ever sure?" he replied, "It's going to be a wrench Corporal – there is no doubt about that – I was attached to that old uniform."

The only trouble with the RAF just now was that it was a bit like the little girl in the nursery rhyme – 'When she was good, she was very, very good, but when she was bad she was horrid!'

The trick was to forget the horrid bits but it was just a bit too soon to be able to do that. A year later and he might have made a different decision altogether. It was a split second decision that would affect the lives of the next generation just as surely as his ancestor's decisions affected his. All he could do was hope he had made the right choices.

He turned his back on his uniform and picked out a three piece suit and a shirt and raincoat. He was even supplied with shoes and socks and underclothes and also a trilby hat.

"I can't see me wearing that!" he laughed, "It makes me look like a spiv – I'll give it to my dad and he can wear it down the garden."

Stan was a standard size and so very few alterations were needed, but it would all still take some getting used to. He had spent every waking moment of the past six years in uniform.

He got himself dressed and surveyed himself in front of the mirror screwing up his nose at what he saw. He was so used to air force blue that he felt as though he was looking at someone else for a minute.

"I feel as though I am done up for a bloomin' wedding!" he laughed.

He picked up the rest of the civilian clothes that had been issued to him and stuffed them in his kitbag.

"Cheerio Corporal, and good luck to you," he said.

"Goodbye Mr. Ratcliff," smiled the young NCO.

Stan flinched like he had been hit – *that* brought it home!

"Ouch!" he smiled as he went out of the door meeting a queue of others who were on their way in for the same purpose.

There was no getting away from it. He did feel odd now that demob had finally arrived. It seemed like a lifetime ago when he had joined and yet, in other ways it had gone so quickly...

When he joined up the first time round, just two days after his eighteenth birthday, he was sent to RAF Cardington. The Air Force then was barely as old as he was and it had been peacetime. Even so, it had still been an adventure.

He had been part of the Guard of Honour sent to France in 1930 when the R101 airship so tragically crashed. It had been his job to escort the 'remains' back to England for burial and he had seen George V in person. What a memorable experience that had been for a young lad who never dreamed he would ever go abroad. He certainly could not have envisaged that he would be back there in a war nine years later! The time had sped by and both his times in the RAF seemed to merge into one.

He smiled wryly to himself as he remembered the arrival of that brown envelope with OHMS written on it just before his wedding as he strode out down past the billets to the Sergeant's Mess in order to say goodbye to some of the blokes. He was thirty-four now and couldn't believe where the time had gone since that first day nearly seventeen years ago.

When he was living through the years the time seemed interminable but now, looking back, the whole of his service life had gone by like lightening. It was funny how the mind could play such tricks – and there had been such progress! He had 'been there' when the RAF was in its infancy and he had been in the 'thick of it' in the War.

Like the bloke in some book he had read at school 'he had seen some of the best of times and the worst of times'.

Now, there was even talk of planes going 'faster than sound' – apparently as a result of the invention of the V1s and V2s. It was an exciting and eventful life and things were moving fast.

However, most of the chaps who were being 'called-up' were fifteen years younger than him, and many of the people of his own age had already left – or were dead! He had missed out on too much already at home and he was not going to miss out on any more, despite his undoubted affection for the RAF. Besides, he couldn't spare any more of his nine lives.

He arrived at the Sergeant's Mess and said goodbye to some of the men who were still waiting to go to stores. Then he tagged along with a group of blokes, all of whom looked slightly uncomfortable in their civilian clothes, and they climbed aboard the RAF bus that was to take them to the train station. The bantering and laughter stopped as the vehicle went through the gates. It was an emotional moment and all were lost in their own thoughts.

Autumn 1945 – Gardener's Cottage

Joan was helping Alice to make pastry men and her young ears were the first to hear the click of the gate and the whistling of her father as he strode down the path.

"There! that looks good Joannie!" said Alice as she proudly surveyed her granddaughter's efforts , "stick some currants on his jacket for buttons and then we'll bake him in the oven like a gingerbread man."

Alice, Stan and Lily.

"Listen Granny, it's daddy!" She jumped down off her box she used to reach the table and the pastry men were temporarily forgotten as the two rushed out to greet Stan as he arrived at the back door and dropped his kit-bag and case on the ground.

Joan stopped short and took a few steps backward, hardly recognising him in his civilian clothes. He looked down at his suit and laughed.

"I know," he sighed, "these are going to take some getting used to – I couldn't believe it was me in the mirror in stores."

"Oh Stanley, you do look smart!" said Alice proudly.

They looked up just in time to see Charles striding across the field as Lily came round the corner from the front of the house, having got off the bus from work.

"Ooh, look at you!" cried Lily as she caught sight of him,

She thought he looked so handsome and he still had the dark sun tan acquired after the years in the Middle East.

"We've got pastry men for tea!" announced Joan, the significance of the occasion totally lost on her. "Well they are not cooked yet but we will have."

Then, as an afterthought, "and you can have some of *my* pastry man Daddy!" It was a gift indeed.

"Well that is very nice!" said Stan, "I'd like one of those."

It had not gone unnoticed that she was suddenly calling him daddy and, little did he know it just then, it was the beginning of very many years of sampling his daughter's cooking and pretending to enjoy it. It was another step towards normality.

He disappeared into the bedroom with his kitbag and came out a few minutes later wearing a pair of grey flannel trousers and an open necked shirt. Nobody would see him in a suit again for a very long time indeed.

Lily was thrilled to have her husband home at last, but it just seemed to accentuate the immediate problem of finding housing.

Stan took a few days to try and get to know his daughter a bit better and then he went to see Mr. Gabriel. Even when he shook hands with the old man he still wondered if he was doing the right thing, but it was too late now. He knew he was going to miss the Air Force, but some sacrifices were worth making.

If he had thought his daughter would 'shadow' him like she did her grandfather he was to be disappointed though – for a while anyway! That was never going to happen straight away. She was either Granddad's 'shadow or Granny's – and if they tired of her following them wherever they went they never showed it! On the other hand, she was quite happy to show her father what she was learning at school, and to teach him how to feed the chickens properly.

"You do it like this!" she said, "Granddad says you must not throw the seed at the poor things, put it in their bowl nicely, and, you must not waste anything."

Suitably 'instructed' Stan did what the child told him to do, and pretended that he was learning something new. *She* thought she had been living there longer than him so she was 'in charge' of things. He looked about the bungalow as he sat down in the spare chair after tea. It seemed to have got smaller. He hoped that the council would not take too long in housing them. Charles went to the mantelpiece and carefully stood up the rainbow picture which had just fallen down.

Stan couldn't help but think that his daughter was capable of doing a much better rainbow now she was a bit older but if his dad wanted that particular one then he wasn't going to comment on it.

"I'll bet you are looking forward to getting back to work my boy!?" said Charles.

"I don't know about that" grinned Stan, "I've got to go to Gabriel's place over at Walton – they are moving back to London now the bombs have stopped dropping!"

His job was going to be delivering wood from the Docks in London to other parts of the country. It would mean sometimes staying overnight as it was a two day trip to take a load to Manchester or Liverpool, but it was just a bit of an improvement on three years in Malta, or Egypt for that matter! In any case, there was no rush. He couldn't believe it, but he had been given ninety-six days paid leave by the RAF!

It was an accumulation of all the time he had not taken off during the six years of the war. In theory he did not have to go to work until December and it was still only September. The Ministry of Defence certainly believed in paying its dues.

From Lily's point of view it was some sort of compensation for all those years when they had not been able to be together at all.

Alice and Joannie came in from feeding the chickens and the room seemed to get even smaller. With a 'start' Stan realised that his parents were getting elderly. When he had gone away they had been, in his eyes anyway, middle aged. Two world wars had taken their toll, especially on Alice. She was still only 66 but she did seem to be so much frailer now. It was time that he and Lily left them in peace and got on with their own lives.

Lily must have read his thoughts.

"I'll get down the Council tomorrow and see where we are on the waiting list!" she said.

"I think you will have a very long wait Lil," said Charles, "They have got thousands to re-house and they will look after the ones that got bombed out first."

"Well maybe we will get a pre-fab." replied Stan.

Their conversation was suddenly stopped by the sound of all the Church bells round about ringing at once. It could only mean that something had happened of great importance. Alice ran outside as Charles leaned over and switched the wireless on.

> *"Victory in the Far East, Victory in the Far East, the Japanese have surrendered!"*

This was the one thing that everyone had been waiting for – it meant that the war had ended completely now. Once again the Union Jacks came out and the sound of the Church bells went on and on. All Joan knew was that it was a bit like it had been just before her birthday when everyone did 'hands, knees, and bumps-a-daisy' in the street,

Charles went to the larder and returned with a bottle of port. Now they could celebrate without feeling guilty.

"Come on Kate," he said to Alice, "Get the glasses out woman!"

It all felt a bit like old Churchill's words again, with a slight difference – "This is not the end of the beginning, but the start of a new beginning."

It would, however, be some time before the magnitude of the huge bombs that were dropped by the Americans on Japan became fully known to everyone, but it was Mr. Atlee who announced that *allied nations across the globe can rejoice in the Victory over Japan.* It really *was* all over. Alice's face went into the folds of her apron and this time it was tears of joy.

Charles looked at his morning paper. He felt like cutting out the front page and sticking it to the wall. It contained a full page picture of the King and Queen and the princesses, together with Winston Churchill plus dozens of pictures of the happy waving crowds.

It was full Victory at last. Churchill was not the Prime Minister any more but nobody cared about that one bit. Mr. Atlee had to take a 'back seat' for a while. It was Churchill that had verbally cajoled everyone through the war and nobody would ever forget it.

Winston Churchill.

Of course, you only had to turn the page to see the pictures of the incredible bombing and then slowly, bit by bit, the news started to come out about the horrors that the Allies had found when they had finally got into the concentration camps and how badly some of our P.O.W's had been treated. Charles threw the paper to the floor in disgust.

"What sort of world do we live in?" he muttered, "It is just unbelievable".

Then he picked the paper up quickly again and put it high up on top of the cupboard. He was determined to protect his nosy little granddaughter from such things and newspapers were kept out of the way and the wireless did not go on until after she had gone to bed. If any papers or magazines were in the house any horrible pictures were quickly torn out.

Even the newspaper that was normally cut up and put in the toilet was checked before it was hung on the string! Toilet rolls were very few and far between – they were among the many things that people had to do without in this time of austerity.

It may have been the end of the war but it was only the beginning of the peace and it would take longer to recover from it than it did to fight it!

10. *"Things are going to be alright"*

1945 – Coxhill Manor

Mr. Christopher Gabriel was the latest owner of the family timber and creosoting business established way back in 1770 by his ancestor.

They had survived one and a half centuries including the First World War comparatively unscathed, but the 'second lot' had been a much more dangerous business for the firm of Gabriel Wade & English. The large scale bombing of Rotherithe Docks had caused Mr. Gabriel to decide to move his offices out to the suburbs until things were back to normal. A V2 landing just yards away was the final straw.

The Water Board, who between the wars were building a large reservoir at Walton-on-Thames, had to stop their work causing their offices, which consisted of two train carriages set in the open fields nearby, to be left empty and in an ideal position to meet Mr. Gabriel's needs. Pretty soon a timber site emerged in one corner of this area and the train carriages, which were already equipped with proper plumbing and even a telephone were used to run the business from. Coke stoves which fed pipes throughout gave each carriage the equivalent to central heating.

Christopher walked out of the back door of his home at Coxhill, just after Victory in the Far East had been announced. Like everyone else, he just enjoyed looking up at the sight of a sky free of aeroplanes, smoke and vapour trails and listening to no other noise but the birds singing.

Now that the war was over he had the pleasing job of transferring his offices back to London. He saw Charles coming through the gate at the bottom of the garden.

"Hello Ratcliff!" said Christopher as he drew nearer to the old man. "How's young Stan?"

"Just getting used to being demobbed!" smiled Charles as he emptied his tools out of his wheelbarrow and touched the rim of his trilby hat.

Mr. Gabriel patted old Charles on the back and watched as he walked on towards the greenhouses.

Then he strolled into the house and was glad to sit down at his desk in the study – he was really starting to feel his age lately. There was a tap on the door and the Butler's daughter, Edna, brought him in a tray of tea and he sipped it gratefully. He was pleased that his son Kit had more or less taken over the family business now and hoped that he might have some ideas about the disposal of the train carriages.

He put a note in his diary to remind himself to say something to the boy, leaned back in his chair and was still deep in thought as his wife came into the room with George.

The dog patiently allowed her to take the lead off and then waddled over to his master and promptly flopped down across his feet.

"Oh get off George you silly old thing." Christopher groaned, "you are like a ton weight!"

Elsie Gabriel rang the bell for Edna to bring more tea in as their eldest son, Kit, entered the room.

"I have had an idea about the train carriages Father!" he said. It was almost as if he had read the old man's thoughts. "They would make good homes for old Coxy and Stan Ratcliff."

Christopher thought for a moment,

"Of course – there is all that concrete area where Stan could park his lorry. It would save on petrol too, because after delivering a load we could let him go straight home instead of coming back to the docks and he can keep in touch on the telephone!"

"You are ahead of me!" replied the younger man.

"Hang on!" cried Elsie Gabriel as she looked up from her book. "All these plans you are making, you haven't even asked the boy yet, and his wife might not *want* to live in a smelly old train carriage!"

"I bet he says yes!" said Kit, "I hope so anyway, I would hate to see those old Pullman trains destroyed. I reckon they could be done up well and Lily won't let them stay smelly, and…" he went on, fired by his own enthusiasm, "there's all those fields for the youngster to play in!"

His mother gave up and finished her cup of tea. She was expecting her other son Ralph for supper and she had plenty to do.

"I think I will go and see cook and leave you men to it!" she laughed.

"I'm seeing him soon," said Kit, "We'll see what he has to say for himself."

Mrs. Gabriel and Edna left the men to their plans.

Autumn 1945 – No.2. Timber Site

Stan rode his motorbike down the quiet leafy Surrey roads to Walton, trying to avoid the pot-holes and piles of rubble. There was very little traffic and it was easy to follow the instructions that his future employer had given him. He drove in through the wide gap in the hedgerow and found himself looking across towards the green 'man-made' hills of the reservoir that were now covered in bushes. There were still a few of the great stacks of wood on the concrete forecourt awaiting delivery to their destinations, and two large empty lorries. It was easy to see that the timber site was in the process of being dismantled and very soon it would revert back to the countryside that it once was.

He propped his bike up at the side of one of two train carriages marked with the legend 'office' in big letters on the single door at the front, and then walked up the steps and pushed the door back. It reminded him of the MT Section in the RAF.

Kit was waiting for him inside along with a couple of other chaps.

"Hello Ratcliff!" he got up out of his chair and came towards him to shake his hand, "come and join us!"

Immediately one of the men went over to the black coke stove in the corner and took a big brown tin teapot from the top and poured some into a mug. For a brief minute it put Stan in mind of the stoves always found in the middle of the wooden billets that he had grown to know so well throughout his wartime service.

"I'm Albert Cox" said his new acquaintance "pleased to meet you."

"Cox is moving into the train carriage next door!" Kit suddenly blurted out. "Do you and your family want this one until you can get a council house?"

Stan couldn't believe his ears. This was totally out of the blue to him and at first he thought his employer was joking. He had hardly had time to get his coat off!

"Well, if you are going to work for me you might as well have a home to live in!" he was going on, "it will be easier all round if you think the wife will like it – I think you may have a long wait for the council!"

Stan knew that.

"I know there is a lot to do to get it habitable" he continued, "but it's warm in the winter, I can vouch for that, and" he waved in the general direction of the back.

"There are two air raid shelters out there that can be used as sheds or for storage – please God we won't need them any more to dodge bombs."

He was impressed. Of course he would have to see what Lily had to say, but he didn't doubt that she would go for it, and doing-it-up would be one way of using some of his leave constructively. He finished his tea and got up and walked down the length of the carriage.

It needed a lot of painting and Lil' would have to make curtains for all the windows, and there were many, but it wasn't half bad. They could do it between them.

There was the one big communal room that they were in now, but then he walked through the sliding door into yet another room of the same size. It was quite big enough for a bedroom with plenty of space for a double bed and even a single as well. At the moment it was full of junk, but he could see the potential.

He could also see that it had once been a very grand train with mahogany walls ingrained with golden scroll patterns. He imagined it carrying the gentry in Victorian times.

"I bet this was posh in its day!" he said as he gazed around the place. Lily, like his mother, enjoyed 'posh'.

There were windows on either side, no doors – these were at each end of the walk-through carriage. He carried on through to the second big room and pulled the next sliding door back. This had once quite obviously been the guards van. It was almost untouched and remained as it once was, with the steel cages still in place for parcels. He was visualising how he might turn this into a bedroom for his daughter. Much as he loved her he was getting a bit fed up with her sharing their bedroom and, quite often, their bed!

Then he went through the last door at the back which led outside. He opened that and found himself looking across open fields with a corn field beyond. He knew immediately the direction he was looking in – North towards Kingston, because he could see the unmistakeable shapes of the huge silver barrage balloons hanging over that town, a remnant of the war that had only completely finished a few days ago.

It had also been raining and he could see the arc of a huge rainbow over the reservoir hills to the west. He suddenly found himself thinking of the rainbow picture and how much his old dad treasured it.

"Well, what do you think old boy?" said Kit as he came up behind him, "There is a catch though – it will probably take until the end of the year before we can move out completely, so it may be after Christmas before you could move in."

"I'll have to show Lily," said Stan, although in truth he had already made up his mind, and not being able to move just yet was a minor detail. There were people still sleeping on bomb sites and in the London Underground because they had nowhere else to go.

"Besides!" went on Kit, thoroughly pleased with his idea "you would be doing me a favour! I won't have the job of getting rid of the darn things!"

That salvaged Stan's pride a bit. If he was doing his employer a favour as well it couldn't be better.

They met Albert Cox as they strode back down the centre of the carriage to the front.

"Looks like we may be neighbours!" he laughed.

The other chaps had already been outside and loaded up one of the lorries. In time, all the timber would arrive by ship at the docks again and be transported from there across the country. There would no longer be any need for this place of comparative safety.

"Right come on now!" said Kit, "and I'll show you my famous air raid shelters made out of water-pipes – I like these!"

Stan followed him round the back of the carriages wondering what his future employer was enthusing about for all he could see were mounds of grass and flowers – until he got closer.. The pipes had been totally grassed over and were now covered with the remains of the late wild flowers. It would have been a perfect camouflage from the air.

One end of the pipe had been sealed off and the other end had a door that padlocked. Once again he cast his mind back to his old RAF base as it reminded him of some of the shelters they had used there.

Kit opened the door as if he was showing off Aladdin's cave.

"Voila!" he cried. "This one will be yours and Coxy will have the other."

The cavernous pipes were big enough for a man to stand inside with a foot to spare and Stan was already visualising his as a home for his motor bike and a workshop. He couldn't help but think that there were many people who wouldn't have minded these for a home, never mind the train carriage as well and he felt really excited about the prospect of having his own place for his small family.

"Bring Lily over when you like to see it," Kit smiled. "By the way!" he grinned "there is one thing!" He pointed in the direction of where a rather mangy looking ginger cat was haughtily crossing the concrete area towards them as if he owned the place.

"That comes with the territory I'm afraid! He is called Ginger!"

Stan tried very hard not to laugh out loud at the obvious name as the old moggy purred and rubbed against his leg.

"I think you have found a friend!" chuckled Coxy as he came past and went into the other train carriage.

"Actually he is no problem," said Kit, "he just lives underneath and he is quiet ancient!"

He looked to where his new employer was pointing. Both trains were about a foot off the ground and set into blocks of concrete where the wheels once were. It kept air circulating underneath so that inside the floor remained dry and warm. It was, though, ideal for storing ladders and providing a spacious home for old pussy-cats. He couldn't wait to get home and tell Lily.

Gardener's Cottage

Joan was unaware of the discussions about her future going on over at Walton. There had been much talk of daddy seeing about a job with Mr. Gabriel

"I am going to see a man about a job!" he had said and then disappeared down the road on his motor bike.

She found it all very confusing because that is what Granny sometimes said when she was only going 'out the back' but she knew who Mr. Gabriel was.

It had been a lovely sunny morning and now she was picking the last of the blackberries along the hedgerow as she waited for Granddad to come out of the gate at the top of the field. Then, quite suddenly, it started to rain, just gently at first, but enough to cause Alice and Lily to run out and grab the child and her bowl of fruit and get her indoors.

"Where did that come from?" panted Lily as she shook the wet droplets out of her dark hair and brushed down her dress,

"The sun is still shining too!" said Joan.

"Oh that means there will be a rainbow!" said Alice, "we'll have a look in a minute when it stops."

The downpour stopped almost as soon as it had started and the three ventured back out to the dampened field that smelt as only damp fields can smell in England.

"Look!" cried Alice "look Joannie, look at that lovely rainbow."

The three stood in the field and stared across towards the farm at the perfect arc going right across the sky.

"Do you know the colours?" said Lily, never a one to let any opportunity to teach her child anything pass her by.

"Yes, red, orange, yellow, green and mauve" she chanted.

"The mauve is actually called indigo!" said Alice, "can you say that dear?"

"In di go!"

The rainbow seemed to get brighter as they stood still and stared at it, and when Charles came through the iron gate on the other side of the field, he looked as though he was bathed in all the colours.

"You know what it means don't you Mummy!?" said Joan as she handed Lily the blackberries she had picked, "it means that things are going to be all right – like it was for Noah and all the animals, and there won't be any 'nasties' anymore."

"Then that must be so!" replied Lily.

She had long since given up trying to work out where her daughter 'got it all from', but she guessed the culprit was even now walking towards them pushing his barrow.

"A train carriage!?" Lily said it like Dame Edith Evans saying "a handbag!!" in The Importance of being Ernest"! She couldn't believe her ears! Her husband was asking her to go and live in a train carriage!

"I'll tell you what!" said Stan, "It's got flush toilet – that's more than your mother has got, and you don't even need to go outside like we do here!"

"Beggars can't be choosers!" laughed Rosa from the sink, where she was washing the blackberries picked earlier.

"They will never be beggars as long as I live and breathe!" retorted Charles. "Still, it might be worth having a look at it Lil' – old Gabriel wouldn't have suggested it if it was no good – he's a decent man!"

"After all, it *is* a Pullman!" smiled Stan, knowing his wife only too well!

The Pullman class trains had been very grand in their day and only the rich travelled in them.

"A Pullman eh?" Lily was beginning to be won over.

"How do you fancy living in a train carriage?" said Stan to his daughter as she came in through the back door, her face still covered in the blue stain from the blackberries that didn't reach the kitchen.

She had been busy throwing a ball against the wall and trying to catch it. Tiring of continually losing it among the flowers, she came indoors just in time to hear the adults all talking about trains again.

"Will it be in the field at the back?" she replied.

"Oh bum!" thought Lily. "This might not be so easy!"

She attacked Joan's face with a wet flannel.

"Well no, not quite," chipped in Charles, "but it is not very far away and you can come and see us whenever you want."

"Will we come and see you in the train Granddad?" she replied, through a mouth full of flannel.

"Well, not the same train as we will be living in!" said Stan patiently, "because if we did that then the furniture would fall all over the place. In another train like the one you went away in before."

He could have bitten his tongue off!

"Oh we went a long way away," she didn't like the sound of this at all, and the tears started to come. "I want to stay with Granddad and Granny!"

"We can see them every Sunday...and," went on Stan, "when you are a really big girl I can take you on the back of my motor-bike."

He flinched as Lily kicked him hard under the table. He wasn't doing very well with his women at the moment!

"Anyway!" she brought the conversation to an abrupt end. "We haven't quite decided yet."

"Come on Joannie." said Charles "come and read your story book to me!"

All talk of train carriages was put to one side as Joan read out loud. She didn't need to look at the words, she knew it all by heart anyway!

"Once upon a time there was a little boy and his name was Little Black Sambo and his mummy made him a beautiful little red coat and a pair of beautiful blue

trousers and his daddy went to the shops and bought him a beautiful green umbrella and a pair of purple shoes…"

"And wasn't little Black Sambo grand?" everybody joined in. She put the book down.

"We have had this story lots of times!" she said "tell me the story about the dancing fairies in the fireplace Granddad!"

"How many times have you had *that* story!?" laughed Charles, "and we have no fire lit anyway!"

Stan was starting to realise that little girls could be very awkward. Apart from Lily, his parents had been the only stability in the child's life for nearly five years. The relationship, particularly, between his daughter and his father was very special indeed.

Whether the fire was lit or not was immaterial – she got her 'fireside story' and all talk of living in train carriages was temporarily forgotten – by her anyway!

Lily put on her warm coat and headscarf and cuddled up behind Stan on the motorbike. It was only about forty minutes over to where the train carriage was, down quiet country roads, but she was glad that the late autumn day was unusually warm. It got cold on the back of the vehicle although he always took it steady when he had a passenger.

In fact it became quite enjoyable driving along looking at the last few red and gold leaves on the trees which fell away with any sudden movement of bird or squirrel in the branches. Stan had to be very careful though – there were many craters and pot-holes and they passed a number of houses that were in ruins from bombs. Rebuilding had barely started and there was very little traffic on the roads other than military vehicles.

She held on to her husband around his waist and looked forward to her first view of what she knew would be their home together. She could tell he had made his mind up to it, and she would go with him even if it were a tin can!

Kit and Coxy were waiting for them as they drove into the yard and it looked as though old Coxy had already made a start on his own train carriage. Lily could see his new home half painted in a light green, and a woman, whom she later found out was Doreen Cox, was busy cleaning the numerous windows.

She felt as stiff as a plank as she leaned on Stan's shoulder and struggled to get off the back of the bike. She looked at the huge concrete area where once the lorries had been parked. Now there was just Stan's and there was little sign that it had ever been a timber site.

Beyond that were the fields and the hills that had been formed as part of the reservoir, now covered in bushes and wild flowers.

"Hello Mrs. Ratcliff!" said Kit. She thought he was a charming man. He was wearing a smart suit and had all the distinguished appearance of one who had come from a privileged background and was used to being in charge.

"Come along dear!" he grinned "It needs a lot doing to it, but you come and have a cup of tea and see what you think."

She meekly followed him to the carriage that was placed at right-angles to Coxy's thereby forming an L shape, but with plenty of space in between the two and climbed up the steps to the front door.

"If you want to powder your nose, it's in there!" said Kit, pointing to their right, just inside the porchway.

She did – it was a cold old ride from Chobham! She went into the W.C. as Kit and Stan moved on through into the main body of the carriage. It wasn't a very big toilet, but it was grand, and it was certainly more than her mother had got. The walls were in dark brown mahogany with a gold leaf design and already she had visualised polishing them up. There was also a small sink so no more using a china bowl and jug for washing.

There was also real toilet paper! True it was very thick and rough and had 'Government Property' stamped all over it, but it was toilet paper all the same – and, it was inside! No more going outside in all weathers – luxury indeed!

However, her heart sank when she joined the others in the main part of the train. What a scruffy old place! All the time she had spent 'in-service' as a teenager rushed back to her as she looked at the windows down either side, all of which were in need of a damn good clean and some net curtains.

Despite that, she had already, mentally, polished the wooden walls and black-leaded the stove in the corner before Kit spoke to her again, and she could well imagine what it could look like once she had got to work and put some 'elbow grease' into it. She knew too, that they would qualify to buy some 'utility furniture'. Only people who had been bombed out completely, or newlyweds, were allowed to have furniture coupons, and as Stan had been sent abroad the day after their wedding they counted as 'newlyweds'.

"Well, what do you think?" said Kit proudly.

Lily could certainly see the potential, but the very idea of living in a train carriage. Well, it was different. She had already decided to agree when Coxy appeared at the door. One side of his face and half his hair were covered in light green paint where he had been running his mucky hands across his head.

"Come and have a look in mine!" he invited. "We have a lot to do but we are getting there!"

Stan and Lily followed him down the steps and round the front of the partially painted No.1 Timber Site. Doreen greeted them at the door just as Kenny, their ten year old son arrived in from school on his bike.

"We have only done in here!" she said, pointing to the cosy living area. "We are still sleeping on camp beds in the other room, but it's not bad is it?"

"Better than the London Underground anyway!" said Kenny with fervour, "it was horrible sleeping there."

It certainly wasn't bad. The windows were sparkling and Doreen had made curtains for all sixteen of them. There was shiny linoleum on the floor and they had put in two 'utility' armchairs and a dining table and chairs. The 'kitchen', such as it was, had been made out of the far end of the carriage with a long trestle table where she had her pastry board and storage jars. They too were able to buy some furniture because they had been bombed out. The utility furniture was very plain. The object was that it used the least and cheapest of wood possible, but Doreen had polished it and made the best of it.

"Oh Stan, isn't that nice!" said Lily, "we could do that!" Suddenly she was fired with enthusiasm.

"The best bit is," said Coxy, "you can do what you want outside because there is no limit. You can build a swing for the kiddie, and look at all the playing space there is." He swept his arm around like a salesman trying to convince a buyer, except that nobody needed convincing.

Doreen was busy at the stove where she was making coffee.

"It's only 'Camp' of course" she said as she tipped the liquid from the narrow bottle. "It will be nice to have proper coffee one day"

"We have a long wait for that" said Stan, "there is so much building to be done and they have to clear the Thames so that the ships can get into the docks – I can't believe how much damage there is everywhere – it's as bad as Malta!"

They were interrupted by Kit as he poked his head round the door.

"Gotta go folks!" he grinned, "Do you fancy moving in Mrs. Ratcliff?

Lily and Stan exchanged glances and nodded.

"Yes, we would love to move here," said Lily, taking over command. She had already mentally cleaned No.2 Timber Site from top to bottom and got her lino and furniture in. Kit and Stan shook hands. It was a 'gentleman's agreement' – they needed no more.

The residents of No.1.Timber Site saw the new residents of No.2. Timber Site off at the door.

"All we have to do now is drag our daughter away from dad and mum," said Stan, "and convince her that she is not being 'vackerated' again".

"She'll be all right," replied Lily with confidence as she climbed on the back of the motor bike. "You just wait and see, – but" she added as he kicked his foot to start the engine, "I am *not* telling people I am living in a train carriage – I shall call it a 'coach'!"

"Snob!" laughed Stan as they set off back along the bumpy roads to Chobham.

Although there wasn't a blackout anymore the street lights were still few and far between so it was as well to get back before it got too dark.

11. *"Our first full year of peace..."*

Gardener's Cottage

"Well at least there should be plenty of squirrels over where Stan is going to live!" grunted Charles as he threw his newspaper across the room in disgust. "The Government are only giving us a recipe for squirrel pie now – what in the name of blue blazes are we coming to – squirrel blasted pie?"

Without even flinching Alice quietly picked the pages up and put them back together again neatly.

"You take no notice of your Granddad Joannie," she said calmly as she saw her granddaughter look up in horror from the table, where she was drawing, "nobody is going to eat any squirrels in *this* house – he is just being very silly again."

She went back to trying to cut some spam into thin slices in order to make it go round.

"Perhaps we are running out of rabbits!" she said "honestly there was nothing at Benham's today – his shelves were empty, except for horse meat – you can have horse meat without coupons you know Charles."

"Oh how wonderful!" he sneered sarcastically.

Joan wasn't sure about eating rabbits or horse meat, although she had been unwittingly eating the former since she was big enough to chew it

"It really does make you wonder who won the war Kate!" grunted Charles again. "It's worse than it was when we were in the middle of it all!"

"We had more food in the 'first lot'," said Alice, "despite the rationing."

"Well, they couldn't darn well bomb our ships from the air so easily then could they?" he retorted.

"Well thank goodness we have the stuff out of the garden," she answered as she started peeling the potatoes, "goodness only knows how the poor souls in the big cities are managing

– well, we know how they are managing don't we – they are starving!"

She was painfully aware that her sisters, who were Londoners, were really struggling and she quite often sacrificed some of her own rations in an attempt to help them with small food parcels.

She began to feel quite guilty peeling the potatoes for she knew that there were many far worse off than the residents of Coxhill – some who would have been happy to eat those very peelings! Instead they were destined to make mash for the chickens.

Rosa came in the back door with a couple of cabbages she had cut and Alice felt even worse for a minute.

"Oh well done Rosa dear!" she said..

"It makes you wonder though," said Rosa, "just how long we are going to have to give coupons for everything."

"Years and years I expect" growled her father as he picked up his paper again to read the rest of the news.

"We must all make sure that we don't waste anything at all!" said Charles, "Don't you women go throwing away any scraps – it can all go in the slop pail and it can go down the farm to help feed the pigs."

He was clearly not in the mood for counting his blessings today!

In fairness, the Government had provided vitamins for the children, including cod-liver oil and vitamin C, and with the honey and the vegetables, Joan did not go hungry at all, but she was acutely aware that people were being told not to waste anything and that it was very difficult for the grown-ups to put food on the table.

The teachers even made their pupils chant a song at school about the housewife's pail to get the message home and the children sang it in the playground and marching down the street.

"Because of the pail the scraps were saved,
because of the scraps the pigs were saved,
because of the pigs the rations were saved,
because of the rations the ships were saved,

because of the ships the Island was saved,
because of the Island the Empire was saved,
and all because of the housewife's pail."

Nobody could accuse either of her Grannies or Granddads of wastage – she never saw them throw anything away. As far as she knew they did not even have a dustbin. What couldn't be burned was buried in the garden.

"Huh – squirrels for dinner – I should say so!" moaned Charles who, by now, had got the bit between his teeth.

Joan was used to her Granddad when 'he was having a moan' and she knew it was always aimed at the newspaper or the wireless and not her. Besides, it seemed to make him feel better sometimes when he thumped the table and got it out of his system.

Suddenly they heard the sound of Stan's motor bike and she threw down her painting brush and ran outside to find her parents. Within a minute Lily and Stan followed their daughter indoors and were telling Charles and Alice how the work was coming on. They had been going to the train carriage every weekend for some time now and today's project had been to finish the main living area so that they could move in.

"Brr! It's cold on the back of that bike." shivered Lily as she took her scarf off and bent down and gave her daughter a kiss.

"Oh that's nice!" she said, looking at the painting. "Look Stan, isn't that a nice painting?"

It was of a house, a square childish house with four windows, one in each corner, and a pointy roof on the top.

"It's not much like our house though!" said Stan "We are going to live in a train carriage." "We'll take you to see it soon."

"Coach!" interrupted Lily, "it's a coach!"

"I hope you have got plenty of squirrels over there!" grunted Charles peevishly.

"Take no notice of him," said Alice, "We are just going to have to stop him getting the newspaper."

"Huh!" he snapped back, "then we won't have anything to wipe our backsides on!"

Everyone dissolved into laughter.

Joan still wasn't very impressed with the train carriage idea though. They had told her lots of times about it but she couldn't really understand how you could get furniture in one.

"Can Granny and Granddad come and live with us in the train?"

"Well no, because they have got their own house and what would Mr. and Mrs. Gabriel do without them?" said Stan.

"But we will visit them, I promise" said Lily quickly as she saw her daughter's eyes well up.

"Promise?"

"And.." said Alice as she put the kettle on the gas stove to boil, "You can come and stay with us whenever you are on holidays from school and help Granddad in the gardens."

"How will Granny manage without me helping her with the chickens?" said Joan, "We won't have any eggs without the chickens."

"Oh I think she will manage all right!" smiled Stan.

"And what about helping her make their mash?" she persisted.

"Tell you what Joannie!" said Charles suddenly, as if he had just thought of it, "when your mother and father have finished making the train carriage nice, you can take two of the chickens with you and you can look after them yourself – how about that?"

"Oh Dad, you can't do that!" said Stan, "not your chickens!"

"I wouldn't have said so if I didn't mean it my boy!" said Charles gruffly, "you have a couple of the best layers and then at least you can have some eggs. There is no bloody meat about!"

"Language Charles!" said Alice gently. It was a lost cause – the squirrels had really got to him.

"What do you say to Granddad?" said Lily.

"Thank you very much." replied Joan.

"As long as you look after them?"

"I will, I promise."

"How's the train carriage coming along anyway Lil'?" asked Rosa. .

"Coach," said Lily, "it's a *coach*, Rosa!"

"We should be in there soon after Christmas,!" said Stan, "there is just a bit more painting to do and" – he looked across to where Joan was busy trying to make towers with the Lexicon cards – "I think we might have to make a swing though."

"Am I going to have my own swing?" She *could* be bought!

"Well, I don't know what we are going to eat for our Christmas Dinner!" grumbled Charles from behind the newspaper. "We had better go fishing!"

He ducked as Alice threw a cushion across the room and it knocked the offending paper out of his hands once and for all.

Christmas was very special, because it was the first time since 1938 Lily and Stan had actually had the festive season together, but there were certainly no goodies in the shops and precious little meat in the butchers.

"I don't know what old Benham bothers opening for!" Charles complained, "He's got nothing to sell us."

Lily paid a visit by herself to her parents, taking with her one or two gifts from her in-laws. There was a bottle of home made wine that Alice had made and some tobacco for Henry. Charles made his own from the plants that he grew in his own garden at the side of the bungalow. The leaves were picked and dried and shredded and the end result was a mixture that he could put in a pipe 'on high days and holidays.'

He wasn't much of a smoker, but he knew Henry was, so he shredded some up and put it in a tin for him. Lily couldn't help thinking that, between the two families, they were ninety percent self sufficient. All they needed was their own sheep for wool and a cotton-field!

Henry Gosley didn't 'do' presents, but he did give Lily a rabbit to take back for Alice to cook and Grace had found Joan a book. It wasn't easy for her mother, Lily knew that.

Henry's idea of a good Christmas was an extra hour in the Sergeants Mess.

Back at the Ratcliff household Charles was careful to make sure that there was no fire in the grate.

"Dad!" cried Rosa "its freezing!"

"Then light the gas fire in your bedroom girl!" was the gruff retort "We can't have a fire tonight and burn Father Christmas's bottom – whatever next?"

"Dad!" laughed Lily "Can't we let him come through the door?"

"What,… and leave it open for eye-tyes and pies to get in as well?" he said, with a twinkle in his eye.

He was clearly having a joke for Joannie's benefit, so the family had to put up with being cold until after she had gone to bed. It was the first year that she really knew who Father Christmas was.

"I wouldn't mind." Rosa whispered to Stan, "but he lit the fire back in the summer, when we didn't need it, just so that he could tell her a fireside story!"

"That's my dad!" laughed Stan with pride.

"Sorry!" giggled Lily as she shivered and wrapped her cardigan around herself. "I'll get her to bed out of the way!"

"Don't forget to hang up your stocking!" said Charles as he gave her a kiss and Alice filled her a hot water bottle.

"I hope Father Christmas will know where I am," she queried, "there are lots of children to visit."

"I think he'll manage dear," said Alice.

Lily found her daughter an old laddered stocking that was beyond repair, although she had no idea how they were going to fill it, but if she knew anything at all of her in-laws, they would have a good go!

The child never disturbed them once she had gone to bed unless she was ill. She slept the sleep of one who had an active day. Therefore, the minute she had said her prayers and had settled down, Charles re-lit the fire and between them they filled a stocking identical to the one that she had left on the end of her bed. All Lily would have to do when she retired was swap them round!

"You sing "Away in a Manger" for us," said Lily as she turned the light out, "then we can all hear you!"

"All right, I'll do that, you listen though!"

She was less than word perfect, but she did her best and it brought a very festive atmosphere to the house as the adults settled down for the evening and listened to the words gradually fading as she fell asleep.

"It will do for me," said Stan acutely aware that he was still 'a visitor' in her eyes. Him and millions of other fathers throughout the country.

"Thank goodness for that!" said Rosa as the flames leaped up the chimney, "the things I put up with for my niece!"

Charles had already disappeared outside and came in carrying huge bunches of holly to put up round the room, and a small fir tree.

"Where did you get that from Dad?" asked Rosa.

"Off the common!" he said triumphantly, "come on you women, you must have some silks and things in your sewing basket – get on with it – make some coloured balls or something, – Stan, put the holly up over the pictures."

Very soon, they had managed to decorate the tree with everything from woollen balls to paper streamers and painted fir cones. There were also a few bits and pieces from previous Christmases – a little fairy doll to go on top of the tree, and some coloured cards that hung down and twirled in the breeze or if you blew on them. Then, by the time they had all finished, the stocking was full and looked like some lumpy old tree trunk with all the mysteries that had been put inside.

There were some sweets from Lily and Rosa's rations, a big red apple from Gabriel's trees and a pear from the same source. The fruit had been wrapped in newspaper and kept in the dark and cold so that it was still usable since being picked many weeks earlier. Also, there was a wooden doll and a toy which, if you squeezed the bottom, it would dance.

Once the silence from the other room assured them that the infant was asleep they put the wireless on and listened to the Carols from Westminster. What a treat that was – to listen to the carols without the sound of sirens in the background or the drone of aircraft overhead.

Satisfied that they had done all they could, Alice set about making cocoa for everyone, as they all wished each other a happy Christmas 1945.

Lily and Stan were rudely woken up in the morning by their daughter jumping up and down on their bed.

"Mummy, Mummy, wake up!" she was shouting. "Look my stocking is all full up, come and see!"

The child delved into one of her mother's precious stockings and looked at all the gifts in turn.

It was a magical moment, but Lily couldn't help thinking ruefully that, because of rationing, the stocking was actually worth more than the gifts inside – even with the ladders!

"Look, how did Father Christmas know that I wanted a yo-yo – look I've got a yo-yo, and some pencils".

She ran around from one to the other showing them what Father Christmas had bought her.

By now, the rest of the household were up and Alice had already 'been out the back' as she called it, to the toilet and was dressed in her best clothes, while Charles finished his shaving ready to go to Church.

Joannie came running through, torn between telling them about Father Christmas and wanting to go 'out the back'. She stopped short at the sight of the tree and the decorations and forgot about both! For a minute anyway!

Then she remembered that she had to go or wet her pyjamas and she was off out into the back yard with Lily following close behind her. It took quite an effort to keep up with her daughter that morning. It was a funny sight to see her trying to accomplish what she came to the toilet to do and talk about Father Christmas at the same time.

"And he must have come right down the chimney with his fairies...because he would have to have fairies to help him...."

Lily made sure that the child was respectable and then followed her back into the house just in time to catch her, as she climbed up on another box at the kitchen sink to wash her hands. Alice was already putting the boiled eggs and toast on the table for breakfast, and cutting the bread into soldiers.

Stan had done some drawings for his parents and for Lily. He was a very clever artist and had tried to capture the sight of the dog-fights going on high in the sky over Valletta Harbour, which he had seen first-hand.

He had drawn them some time ago but thought they might make good Christmas presents.

Also among the pictures was a beautiful drawing of Lily herself 'posing' on the green hills of Surrey before war was declared. She was half sitting, half lying, propped up on one arm on the grass, wearing a white dress with red spots on it. He had copied it onto a piece of card and coloured it in.

"Oh look at that Mum!" said Rosa "isn't that good?"

"I think he has flattered me," said Lily coyly, "I am not as slim as that anymore!"

In fact she was a very pretty woman with a slim figure and dark hair which she normally wore wrapped around in a big curl around her head which was the fashion of the day. Stan had caught her attractiveness and clear skin perfectly.

"Look at this picture that your daddy has done of mummy!" said Alice proudly, "Isn't he clever Joannie?"

Charles put Stan's picture in a place of honour next to the rainbow one on the mantelpiece and there they would stay for a very long time indeed.

Everyone went to Church as usual and this time the bells could ring out and nobody worried about the lights being on. Joan went as well because her school were singing 'Away in a Manger' at the side of the crib.

Each of the children took tea towels with them to wear on their heads tied round with ribbons and all the adults had very wet eyes by the time they had finished singing.

For the first time in six years the whole family were together as Stan's other sister Doris, Harry and Roger joined them for Christmas Dinner. Roger at three and a half was a year younger than his cousin.

"My, you have grown my darling!" cried Alice as she gave her other grandchild a big cuddle, "You will soon be as tall as Joannie – and look at all your lovely curls!"

He did have a mass of beautiful fair curls which Lily thought were totally wasted on a boy.

Roger.

Doris had not come empty handed. Nobody ever went anywhere without taking their 'rations' with them, so she had brought a couple of ounces of butter and a bit of tea and she had also saved her coupons and made a cake.

"Oh that's lovely Doris my dear," said the delighted Alice as she gave her youngest daughter a kiss.

Charles still had a bottle of sherry that he had kept from the previous year and he poured everyone a small tot, and Rosa put a plate of mince pies on the table.

"There you are!" she said, "It doesn't look as though any of us will starve today after all – we'll go back to the bread and dripping tomorrow!"

Joan was much too big for a high chair now so her younger cousin had the use of that while she sat in her usual place high up on two big cushions at the side of Granddad.

"Let us say grace," said Charles, "Put your hands together children and close your eyes."

Both Charles and Alice insisted on saying grace every time the whole family were together.

"For what we are about to receive may the Lord make us truly thankful," said Charles.

"Amen" responded everybody.

As usual Alice had excelled herself. There was chicken and a wide variety of vegetables, but the children were mostly impressed by the Christmas pudding which was full of fruit and covered in brandy butter. She had even found two sixpences to put in it for them to find and Doris carefully mashed it up so that the coins were partially visible to the 'untrained childish eye'!

"We don't want anybody to choke do we?" she grinned, "I don't want to have to bang your backs!"

A sixpence was a large amount of money to a small child.

"Spend some and save some!" said the ever practical Lily, immediately causing Charles to burst into song as Alice collected the empty plates up.

"I've got twopence to spend,
and twopence to lend,
and twopence to take home to my wife!"

All too soon Doris and Harry had to go though. The snow was coming down and settling quickly. They wanted to get across the common on their bikes before it got too bad,

Charles and Alice came out to wave them off.

"Happy New Year when it comes!" said Alice as they strapped Roger onto the back of his mother's bike and made sure he was tucked up warm and cosy.

"Yes, Happy New Year to you all."

They would be across the common and home within half an hour and did not need to worry about the black out anymore.

"Come on Joannie!" said Alice to her granddaughter, "we have some chickens to feed."

Lily wrapped her up in her big coat and pixie hood and stood with Stan and watched her as she ran behind her grandmother down to the chicken run. Christmas or no Christmas the birds still had to be fed with potato mash made from peelings, and all the time they were laying they were spared the fate of the rabbits.

Joan suddenly remembered that they had chicken for dinner and quickly checked to make sure that they were all still there! They were, so she was satisfied that their meal had come from elsewhere. As long as the birds were laying they were more useful to the family alive than dead. If they stopped then she knew that Granddad would show no mercy.

For Stan it was the end of a perfect day. Just being here with the folks beat all the rushing around and the activity in the Sergeant's Mess at Egypt or Malta, especially Malta!

To see his child hanging up her stocking and chattering about Father Christmas was the icing on the cake as far as he was concerned. He still missed the RAF life – after all it was still only three months since demob, but he knew where his priorities lay. There was only one thing that could be better than this and that was to have a Christmas with his wife and child in his own home – and he would, next year – for definite.

On 31st December 1945 Charles opened a bottle of Port he had been saving for the occasion.

"Here's to 1946 – our first full year of peace." He raised his glass in the air and everyone followed. They were words which, no doubt, were echoed throughout the country.

12. *"Number 2 Timber Site would do..."*

Winter 1946 – No.2. Timber Site

It took two ounces of pear drops, a 'three penny bit', a solemn promise that she could go back and visit Granny and Granddad any time she wanted and sole responsibility for feeding the two chickens, but a 'deal' was struck when the time came for Joan to eventually move house.

Alice had been used to Lily and Stan disappearing on the motor-bike every weekend over the winter, but inevitably the time came when they would go on public transport so that they could take their daughter with them and they would not be coming back to live with them again.

"You be a good girl Joannie!" she said as she squashed the pear drops into her granddaughter's small hand. Sweets were still rationed and would be for a good many years yet. They were precious.

"I'll come back next week Granddad!" said Joan as she clutched the sweets tightly. "We need to pick the diddy-dottems you know!"

"Quite right too!" grinned Charles. The grapes would not be ready for months but he didn't say anything. Once she had settled down at her new home she wouldn't even think about diddy-dottems. The only person who did not know that was her!

Going on the bus and train was nothing new and it was only a few stops down the line to where the train carriage was situated.

They struggled down the steps from the station when they arrived at their destination and out onto the long straight unlit road that lead to the reservoirs and No.2 Timber Site. Stan had the job of carrying the heaviest cases and Lily took responsibility for the child as she ran down the road ahead of them. It was a half hour walk with a small person, first running and then dawdling, but it felt like more and they were very glad that it was fine weather.

Eventually they reached their turning and walked through the wide entrance with the two train carriages on their right, and there was Coxy out to greet them.

"Hello everyone!" he cried. He looked down at the child, "and, welcome to your new home madam!"

She looked about and was favourably impressed. There was already a lot of potential for playing among the iron pipes left behind by the water-board, and the, seemingly endless, miles of green grass and hills covered in wild flowers. To their left, separated off in another field, by a narrow wire fence, were two brown horses. They both ambled over and looked at the new arrivals inquisitively. In an instant she was at the fence, reaching up on tip toes to pat their warm faces.

"That's Sandy and Brandy!" said Mr. Cox, "They have just been brought out of their winter quarters ready for the spring and summer – they keep the grass down.

"Can I feed them?"

Stan had his eye on the other end of the horses though – they would make good manure for the garden.

"Hurry up!" called Lily, ever anxious to get on with things and already climbing the steps to No.2, "We have a lot to show you before bedtime."

Stan helped Joan to jump up the steps behind her mother and while Coxy tagged along behind assisting with their cases.

"Whew, I'm pooped!" gasped Lily, "all I want is a sit down and a cup of tea!"

"I'll leave you to it," said Coxy, and disappeared in the direction of his own home.

When her father pulled the sliding door to one side Joan saw it all decorated and finished and ready to live in for the first time. She had no conception of the work that had gone into making it that way.

"Oh it's lovely!" she shouted, and ran down the living area. "It's like a real house!"

Lily had polished the walls until they gleamed and made curtains for every window. They had bought 'utility' furniture, and although it was dark wood, it all seemed to look right in the carriage somehow.

There was a sideboard with a vase of flowers and the ornaments that Stan had brought back from Malta, and a dining table and chairs, and two armchairs. It was warm and cosy, and even Joan's toys were in place, sitting on a shelf, waiting for her attention. They had certainly worked some 'magic' in a very short period of time!

Stan slid back the door into the bedroom and she saw her parent's familiar double bed and her own camp bed in the corner with the dressing table in between. The only thing left to be done was to put the sheets and covers on them.

"Where did those come from?" she cried. She was sure that they had been at Granddad's when they had left this morning.

"Ah, we've got fairies!" said Stan with a chuckle.

"Come this way!" called Lily, who was really enjoying herself by now, "I've got something else to show you."

Joan followed them both through to the 'Guards Van' which was still full of rubbish. It was the only part of the train carriage that had not been touched.

"We haven't had time to do this bit yet" said Stan "but when we do, it will be your very own room – what do you think of that?"

"It's just a 'glory-hole' at the moment!" said Lily as she followed along behind, "but we will make it nice for you one day and you will have your very own furniture."

She had little time to concern herself about that because already she was following Stan through the rear door and down the steps to the outside.

"This way," he announced grandly, "there's more!"

"Now, close your eyes!" he smiled, "no peeping now."

He guided her out into the sunshine and took a few paces. "You're not peeping are you?"

"No! No!"

"Right, you can open them now!"

She opened her eyes and found herself face to face with the most beautiful and grandest swing that she had ever seen in her life. Stan had made it with creosoted poles acquired from Gabriel's Timber firm, and strong heavy-duty rope of the sort used to make the loads secure. The seat was lovingly made out of a sanded and polished piece of oak, and the whole thing set firmly in concrete into the ground. She didn't know it but it had taken both the strength of her father *and* Coxy to get the poles in position in the cement. Stan was very strong and muscular but even he could not manage it on his own.

It was quite big enough for Lily to sit on and put the youngster on her lap and swing high into the sky and she didn't lose any time in doing so! Making up the beds could wait.

"Wheee!" shouted Lily as they soared upwards with Stan laughing at their antics. "Hold tight!"

When the swing was up to its highest height they could see right across the fields and even to the road in the distance and the fields beyond that.

"Wheee!" squealed Lily again, in her element as she caught up on her own lost childhood.

They would have stayed there all day if they could, but then Joan spotted something else.

"Oh it's Granddad's chickens – stop, stop!"

Lily, reluctantly, scraped her feet along the ground and brought the swing to a halt. Charles had been true to his word. He had given Stan two of his finest hens and they had already been brought over from his bungalow in a wooden crate. He had made a large run for them out of chicken wire and a wooden house for them to lay their eggs in.

She ran to where she had spotted the coop and recognised both birds straight away. They were Granddad's best brown hens and they were strutting about as if they already owned the place.

"You will have to be in charge of feeding them!" said Lily, "don't forget you promised your Granddad."

Stan looked on in amusement as the youngster ran around, not knowing what to do first!

"We have decided to call them Genevieve and Jacqueline," laughed Lily, "After your dad's French girlfriends!"

Joan didn't have a clue what her parents were talking about but was quite happy to call them whatever they wanted to call them, even though she couldn't say it very well. She would find their corn and feed them straight away.

"Hello!" Stan said suddenly "here's old Ginger."

The old moggy crawled out from underneath the carriage and sidled up to see what all the fuss was about. She bent down to stroke his head and the chickens were temporarily forgotten.

"We'll have to find him some milk," said Lily, "poor old thing."

She walked into the little porch at the front of the train to where Stan had built a 'safe' in the cool. It was covered in wire mesh to keep the flies out and the milk kept in an earthenware container inside it.

"Come on you mangy old moggy!" she called, "Let's find you a drink, and then we can have our tea – such as it is."

The cat ran off behind Lily and sat patiently while she found a saucer.

"I don't know what you are going to eat though puss!" said Lily as she gradually came back to reality, "You'll have to catch your own for there won't be any scraps left here."

Pullman Train similar to that at 2 Timber Site.

Joan felt her father's large hand hold on to her small one and guide her back into the main part of the train carriage and immediately the bond which had been deprived him for so long was there. As far as she was concerned, as long as they were not going to be evacuated any more and she could see her grandparents whenever they wanted, then No.2 Timber Site would do!

Lily disappeared into the tiny kitchen to try and find something to eat. Fortunately the chickens had laid two eggs and there was always the bread and milk, The egg ration was only one per person per week so they considered themselves very lucky to have their own birds. Rationing seemed to get worse instead of better but they always seemed to overcome it somehow.

Stan knew what *his* first job would be. He would have to get cracking in the vegetable and fruit garden which would consist of half their diet Lily was under no illusions either – it would be a struggle but together they would manage.

When Joan awoke the following morning she spent a few minutes wondering where she was. The surroundings were strange, but it didn't take long to get familiarised again as she sat up and looked across at the big double bed where her father was propped up on the pillows enjoying his last Sunday morning before going back to work. She could hear her mother bustling away in the living area making a pot of tea and singing as she did so.

"Here you are, wakey wakey!" she called as she came through carrying the tray and set it on the side table as the child climbed up on the big bed and crawled in between them.

"No peace for the wicked!" said Lily "what are you after young lady?"

"Cup of tea!" was the immediate answer.

Stan leaned over and poured his daughter out a weak cup of tea and the three of them sat up in bed as the dawn streamed in through the carriage windows. For the first time in five years he felt as though his child had forgiven him for being away all that time. She would be much older and wiser before she realised that it really hadn't been his fault at all.

"Come on, you've got a proper place to wash now!" said Lily jumping out of bed, "no excuses any more."

She marched her charge down to the little toilet with the proper sink and washed the sleep from her eyes with the flannel. Neither of them had ever had an indoor toilet before.

"Clean your teeth!" she went on "You can do that yourself, but I shall want to look!"

She did as she was told and stood still while Lily brushed her hair and put a bow in it. Then she ran back into the main room and pushed her face against the window where she spotted the familiar sight of the lorry parked outside all ready for the working week. It all looked so inviting and she couldn't wait to get outside and inspect everywhere else.

When she finished her porridge and finally climbed down the steps she found herself on the concrete play area and, once again, didn't know what to do first – feed the chickens, tend to the horses, stroke the cat or go on the swing. But that wasn't all – there were the 'iron things'. These were actually huge black iron pipe sections left behind by the water board, in a pile, at the end of the concreted area. All were about six feet in circumference and two foot in depth. Some were on their sides forming huge circles like deep sided Olympic rings, and others were secured into the ground on their ends like a magical circle that you could run in and out of – or, with the help of an adult you could climb right onto the top and slide down the side. The whole lot together formed a very solid, very large, combination of a climbing frame, a slide, and a number of dens.

Then, beyond this 'wonder' there were the green fields that stretched right across to the hills of the reservoir, which, at this early stage of exploration, had yet to be discovered.

The huge reservoir was surrounded in a circle by two man-made hills with a valley in between them. The original plan to cover them with landscaping had become acutely necessary when it became obvious that war was imminent.

Nobody wanted the water supplies for thousands of homes to be bombed so every effort was made to make them look like natural lakes and hills from the air. Now, 'mother nature' had added to the efforts made by the Water Board in the thirties and the hills were covered in numerous varieties of flowers, hawthorn and blackberry bushes, and also lilac and apple trees all mixed up together.

In the shadier valley between the two hills around the circumference of the 'lake' there were bluebells, coltsfoot, primroses and pussy-willow. You could walk around the top of either hill, a distance of about three miles and look down on the huge expanse of water they surrounded, where ducks and swans gathered undisturbed. If you had plenty of energy you could run down one hill, gaining momentum to take you across the valley and half way up the hill on the other side.

Still to be discovered, but equally important for a small child, was the stream for collecting frog's spawn in jars with the little bridge across it where you could play pooh-sticks and where water irises grew. The word 'bored' was not in this child's vocabulary and there was too much to do to dwell on the absence of Granny and Granddad for too long.

Stan stood and watched and found himself laughing out loud as she ran this way and that, not knowing what to do first.

"Don't go too far away!" he shouted.

Ginger took an impatient look at all the activity and disappeared under the train carriage for some peace and quiet.

Stan glanced up at the sky. It was clouding over and it looked like rain, but he felt contented. The rich could keep their mansions – he was happy with his train carriage. He walked into the living area where Lily was already busying herself with peeling potatoes for dinner. It would be spam again – he knew that, but things would improve, he knew that too. After all – his dad had said so – and his dad was rarely wrong.

In the meantime, his young daughter had all the time in the world to get used to the place.

With all that there was to do and visits to both lots of grandparents the time went by very quickly. Spring was soon over and the long hot summer of 1946 began. Lily could hardly believe it, and yet, so much had happened. It was barely a year since the end of the war and everyone was still struggling for normality. Normality, for the adults anyway, would be a long time coming!

Within a few weeks Joan started at the little infants' school though there was hardly time to settle in before they were breaking up for the summer anyway. Nevertheless, for one who had already been to two schools it was all part of the general adventure and she was quick to make friends. Lily spent every spare moment making and mending clothes. She couldn't get away with putting her daughter in dungarees any more – not now she was going to a proper school.

Stan settled into his work delivering wood, creosoted or otherwise, to destinations all over the country on behalf of his employers and drove for long hours in his efforts to feed his family and save for a holiday at the seaside. It was a holiday that seven long years ago he had promised Lily they would have. The holiday that should have been their honeymoon.

He did sometimes think about the RAF and what 'might have been' but those moments were fleeting. It seemed hard to believe that this time last year he was still in Egypt.

Half way through the school holidays Stan came in from work waving a piece of, what looked like, white flimsy paper in the air.

"Look what *I've* got!" He stood in the doorway and held a five pound note up high in triumph. "Holiday money – *we* are going to the seaside."

"What's that?" asked Joan, who had never seen a five pound note before.

As it happened, Lily couldn't remember ever having seen one either.

"Ooh Stan, let me look!" she cried as she tried to reach it from out of his hand – a real fiver!"

She got it off him and held the large note gingerly in both hands as if it would bite her.

"Have a good look" said Stan, "It might be a while before we see another one – we are off to the seaside so get your bucket and spades."

He was due a week's paid holiday, so, unbeknown to Joan, arrangements had been made to go and stay with Edie and Wilfred at Margate. Alice's sister and brother-in-law had given up their place in the Channel Islands once the Germans had left and had, almost immediately, bought an old 'bed and breakfast' on the Kent Coast which they called 'Wilmarede' made up from the first three letters of theirs, and their daughter Margaret's names.

"Old Wilf has his eye to business!" Charles had said, when he first heard of their idea so soon after the war had ended. Wilfred did, indeed, take chances. Going to Jersey at the end of the First World War had been a case in point as far as Charles was concerned. After all, although the place was British, it was only just off the coast of France!

"It's too damn near 'the froggies' for my liking," he had exclaimed.

Everyone had held their breath when the place had been occupied by the enemy, but Edie and Wilfred had tried to keep 'themselves to themselves' and although it had been pretty awful, they had managed to get through it together and left as soon as they could.

"We are not being 'vackerated are we?" said Joan, getting suspicious the minute she saw the suitcases re-appearing. "I don't want us to be 'vackerated!"

"No, we are not going to be evacuated!" laughed Stan "look, I have a five pound note and we are going to stay for a few days with your Great Aunt Edie."

She was very impressed with the five pound note, especially when she realised that it represented five whole one pound notes. She knew what a one pound note was and if Great Aunt Edie lived near the seaside then that was all right.

It was very warm weather and really the first year that anybody could go to the coast again. Children of Joan's age had never been before in their lives and the only thing they knew about it was from picture books. Of course, Wilfred knew this, and so his investment would eventually become very profitable. He was certainly the businessman of the family. Not that it would cost Lily and Stan anything. All they would have to do was to take their ration books and contribute towards the cost of the food.

Any misgivings that Joan had disappeared first, when she realised that her father was going to be with them, and second when they boarded the packed train with hundreds of other families.

Every child was carrying a bucket and spade. It was a long journey which involved a change of trains in London but everybody had the comradeship which only comes from being together with people that have all been through a shocking experience and who were all going to the seaside together.

This time though she *did* notice the bombed out buildings on either side of the railway line and the piles of bricks everywhere with flowers and weeds growing up through them. It was an awesome sight.

Every so often she nodded off to sleep, and then once, Lily had the job of escorting her daughter down the long corridor of the train to the toilet. Both Lily and Stan marvelled at how crowded it was. It was as if people could not get to the seaside fast enough to make sure if it was still there! The previous year the beaches had been covered in barbed wire, and, in many cases, land mines. Even now, there were only certain seaside resorts you could go to, and Margate was one of them.

Summer 1946 – 'Wilmarede', Margate

Edie was there to greet them when they finally arrived at the house which was just a few streets away from the sea front.

"Hello dear!" she beamed, "Gosh, you are a big girl now!"

She was the image of her sister Alice, if a little bit tubbier. Even the pinny and the smell of baking and lavender were the same. They learned that Wilfred had got himself a job at 'Dreamland', which had just opened up again that year, but in his spare time he was helping his wife to 'do up' the house ready for their eventual visitors.

"He is on the tubs!" said Edie mysteriously.

Nobody knew what she meant by that, not even Stan, but they would find out by the end of the week.

The following day they went down to the beach and all the children were totally overawed. Most had never seen so many crowds of people, all trying to find a place to put a deckchair, and people milling about by the pier having their photos taken and buying ice-cream cornets and sticks of rock. Stan paid a man two pennies and came away with deckchairs for Lily and himself.

"This is too big for you!" he said to Joan "You can sit on the sand and make sandcastles."

She did not need telling twice and could hardly contain herself as Lily stripped her off and dressed her in her knitted bathing costume.

"I want to go in the sea!" she cried, "Come on everyone, let's go in the sea."

Looking around, it was hard to imagine that little more than a year ago the beach would have been totally deserted. It was well known that one of the last V2's had hit the Kent Coast killing about sixty people all in one go. Stan removed his trousers to reveal his bathing costume underneath. Lily though, declined her daughter's kind offer for a trip down to the water.

"Go on you two." she smiled, "I'll stay and keep our place."

Not that she was concerned about getting anything pinched. In 1946 a place on the beach was far more important to people than wanting what anybody else had.

The little girl ran off down the sand with her father close behind her, and then came to a grinding halt when her toes hit the lapping waves for the very first time in her life.

"Oh it's cold!" she laughed, jumping up and down in about an inch of water.

"Come on, don't be a baby, you'll get used to it."

He ran fast into the sea and within a few seconds had ducked underneath and was swimming away under the waves. Then, as she watched he popped up and swam back towards her. He stood up to his waist in the water and wiped his dark wavy hair back off his face.

The suntan that he had acquired in Egypt had hardly faded at all and his forearms and face looked almost black as he walked the rest of the way to where she was and grabbed hold of her outstretched hands.

Gradually, she plucked up the courage to venture further in and, following the lead of the children around her, began to jump the waves as Stan lifted her up over them. In a short time she got used to the water and then the difficulty would be in getting her out again.

"Time to get dried!" he said eventually, "We have left your poor mum on her own for quite long enough."

"Look, I can swim!" said Joan as she lay on the ground on her stomach."

"Come on, we can make a sandcastle and I'll buy you a stick of rock!"

He had remembered that she *could* be bought!

Margate 1946.

By the time they re-joined Lily the sea-water had done its worst to the knitted bathing costume. The wool had stretched and it was hanging around her knees, but she didn't mind. A stick of rock was a treat indeed and kept her quiet for five minutes. In fact, this too was a first. She could not remember ever having such a thing before and there was still time left for an ice cream cornet if she played her cards right.

That evening they did find out what Wilfred's job was 'on the tubs'! Dreamland, Margate's Pleasure Park, which had closed before the war, had just re-opened again and the tubs were like large round half-barrels which you could sit in. They transported you through a wonderland of darkened passages with brightly lit fantasy scenes on either side.

One minute you were in pitch black and then the next you came upon a lit-up scene from 'Alice in Wonderland', or from 'Mother Goose' or 'Hansel and Gretel'.

Round and round the passages the tubs went, sometimes slow and then, suddenly, fast, and then a swoosh along the water and there, Wilfred would be, ready to catch you and help you out.

"There you are," said Wilfred, "Did you enjoy that!"

"Oh yes!" she squealed.

"Well, have another go then!" he laughed and, before Stan or Lily could protest, he pushed them back in and gave the tub a kick, and off it went around the route again without them paying anything at all.

Stan's Aunt Edie and Uncle Wilf' didn't talk much about when the Germans' took over the Channel Islands, but it was quite clear that it had been very frightening. They waited until Joan was in bed before they did speak about it a little bit.

"Just to go outside and see them marching down the street, or laughing on the corners, was enough." said Wilf'. "They totally took over all the key jobs – we were just lucky that they seemed to leave us alone to run the cafe."

"Not that there was much to sell." grumbled Edie, "We were starving most of the time!"

"We were not allowed to even have a wireless." said Wilfred, "We didn't have a clue what was going on, and we would have been put in prison if they had found one."

"There were so many people that just 'disappeared' overnight," said Edie as tears filled her eyes. "People just uprooted and shipped off to Concentration Camps.

"But why didn't you leave with the evacuation Auntie?" said Stan. "I was in Plymouth with the RAF picking up hundreds of people who had left the islands."

"Wilfred wouldn't leave," she replied, "and I wasn't going without him – he is not much but he is all I have got".

"Anyway, we had been there a long time." said Wilfred ignoring his wife's usual insult. "Nearly twenty years – it was our home – we did send Margaret though – she went to the mainland and she got herself a job up North."

Stan had almost forgotten about his cousin who was grown up now.

"Oh it is all just awful" declared Lily, the families that have been disrupted and worse!

The last time Stan had seen his Aunt Edie he had been a child, although Rosa had gone to the Channel Islands in happier times to visit them in 1930. Edie was totally grey now but, unlike her sister Alice, she had blue eyes. As it happened, what little bit of hair that Wilfred had left, was fair and he too had blue eyes. They were convinced that it was a contribution towards their salvation. Anybody who looked remotely Jewish had been rounded up and shipped off to Germany, and they had lost very many friends that way.

Stan thought of Rosa's dark colouring and shuddered. Good job *she* hadn't decided to stay there and make it her home which she easily could have done at the time.

"Oh don't talk about it any more!" said Edie, her eyes starting to fill up again, "it was just too dreadful for words."

"Well, thank God they didn't get to the mainland." said Wilfred, a touch sarcastically.

Everybody had felt very bitter and neglected when the evacuation of the Islands had stopped, but it must have been a truly difficult decision for those in charge. However, as it turned out, it had been the right one. If Hitler had reached the mainland because troops were pre-occupied with the Channel Islands it just did not bear thinking about. They had to be sacrificed for the greater good.

The conversation ended and Edie and Wilf never spoke about the subject again, but Churchill's words "Never in the field of human conflict….." reverberated through Stan's brain for the umpteenth time that year and he felt as though he was in the middle of a giant jig-saw puzzle. Each day, another piece was fitted in.

He lost count of the number of times he repeated to himself "*we didn't realise how close we came to invasion…*" In fact there were times when he could be seen shaking his head and voicing his thoughts out loud. "We did not realise how close we came…!" It was a thought that stayed with many of his generation forever.

1946 – No.2. Timber Site

The summer of 1946 was a very special time. On warm evenings the family could sit outside on deckchairs that Stan had made himself and watch the evening primroses that grew all around the 'iron things' as they opened up to the moon. All day they had kept their flowers closed, but then one by one they showed-off as dusk began to fall.

If Joan was able to 'push it' long enough she also got to stay up and see the eerie sight of stars in a sky which was totally clear of searchlights and completely silent. There were just trillions of them in a sky so clear and peaceful that occasionally you could see a 'shooting' star whiz across and then disappear over the horizon behind the reservoir hills. The only thing to disturb the peace might be an occasional owl or bat circling about or a quick rustle as Ginger found a mouse.

There were no aircraft in the skies of any description and even the fact of sitting outside at night at all was special, particularly when you are five and your father knows a lot about the different stars and he had used his ration coupons to buy some sweets.

"Look, see those four bright stars there." he said, "the ones with the handle on them. That is the 'Plough' and, look, that one over there, the one with the sword, that's Orion."

It was still a novelty to be able to leave the lights on and have nobody reminding you that there was a black-out. However, it would be a novelty for a different reason when they had black-outs caused by power cuts.

Nevertheless, a little screwed up bag of toffees, a deckchair all to yourself in the twilight, and your daddy by your side can make the world into a very special place indeed.

13. *"I'm glad that you were not left in a 'foreign field'…"*

Autumn 1946 – No.2. Timber Site

Lily walked back along the road from where she had just deposited her offspring at the little Infant's School at the start of the Autumn Term. It was a 'good old step' down the long road away from the fields and the reservoir towards where the Infant's School was. She had to remind herself that this was Joan's third school and yet she was still only five.

It wasn't a bad walk though, if lengthy, as there were very few cars to worry about and no buses – petrol rationing had put paid to that and would do so for a long time to come. In fact, petrol was so scarce that only commercial vehicles and doctors were seen on the roads. It even got to the point where fuel used for industry was dyed red so that it could not be sold to private motorists on the black market.

She cut through the hedge and across the field where the horses were and let herself into the empty train carriage. It was odd to suddenly be alone in the place after the holiday, but there was plenty to do and she had never been happier. She had just called in at the doctors and now had some great news for Stan. It had been confirmed that she was pregnant. She couldn't wait to tell him. This time she would be able to give him the news personally instead of by censored mail that took weeks to get to its destination.

Like her daughter, she didn't know what to do first. She took a huge amount of pride in her home and the place was spotless. To her, polishing the mahogany walls until they gleamed like mirrors was not a chore but a labour of love.

Then there were the blackberries – she couldn't wait to get over on to the hills and pick as many as she needed. She loved picking the fruit but they would have to be bottled for the time being. The sugar ration went nowhere so jam was out of the question. She had a large selection of Kilner jars which she had collected over the years and some that Alice had given her and she took pride in seeing them stuffed to the brim and arranged in rows on the wooden shelves that Stan had made for them.

Of course, everything she wore was going to get tighter so she would have to dig out her old maternity wear from five years ago. Stan had already got his eye on the 'Guards Van' at the end of the coach as a new bedroom for Joan, which under the circumstances, was just as well, Her little corner in their room would be taken up by the new baby. There was much to do.

Lily put Housewives Choice on the wireless and busied herself doing her chores, while she listened to the singing of her favourite crooner, Donald Peers. It was very easy to count her blessings. Considering this was a train carriage, she felt she was not doing so badly at all. She had a flush toilet, a proper little kitchen with running water, and warm pipes than ran right round the walls, heated by the coke stove – that is, if you could get the coke! That though was a minor detail, as Stan was quite happy to bring logs home that he had scavenged from the 'common'. He was not a man to let his family go cold and so, on this autumn day in 1946 she felt very satisfied with her lot and would not swap places with the King himself.

Of course, it was not always going to be this easy. She knew that come the winter it would be hard work especially being pregnant, but she would cope as long as she had Stan by her side.

She didn't think there was any kitchen chore harder than being a scullery maid. She got busy peeling some spuds and tried not to get too impatient as she looked at the clock and waited for him to come home so that she could relate her news.

Joan had been given her tea and was busy feeding the horses their own hay, which they could *quite* easily reach for themselves, when her father's lorry finally came trundling around the corner. She waved to him and watched as he jumped down from the cab slamming the door shut behind him as he gave her a wave. He was across concrete area and into the train carriage in just a few strides while she tried to decide between continuing to feed Sandy and Brandy or following him.

Sometimes, if she sat at the table, he would give her a small portion of dinner from his plate even though he knew quite well that she had already had hers. She therefore thought that now might be a very good time to leave the horses and go and see what he had to eat today. It could be macaroni-cheese like she had and she wouldn't mind some more of that.

She climbed up the steps and found her parents giving each other a big hug and looking very happy indeed and it looked as though her father had completely forgotten his dinner altogether which was a bit disappointing.

"We are going to have a new little baby." said Lily, "What do you think of that?"

She did not think very much at all and was a bit miffed that nobody was eating any dinner yet. Her friend Pauline had a new baby and it couldn't even say mama and Pauline said that it would be ages before he would be able to do so.

Of course, there were dolls that could say mama but she didn't have one. Not many children did – toys were not a priority, even for those with money, in 1946. Besides she wasn't sure where they would get a baby *from* when they lived in a train carriage. She thought that feeding the horses and collecting the manure to help the plants grow better was much more important than any babies that might take up her mother's time. She hesitated for a minute and then got her priorities right as it didn't look as though any macaroni cheese was coming her way.

"Can I have my bucket and spade!" I'll collect some manure!" was all they got in reply to their momentous news.

Stan and Lily looked at each other and burst into peels of laughter that went totally over their daughter's head.

"Go on with you – you can have some of my macaroni-cheese," said Stan kindly, knowing his daughter only too well.

"That is if you go and wash your hands first," added Lily hastily.

She did as she was told. The manure would still be there tomorrow – the dinner might not.

The conkers were already forming on the trees when the new term started and the walk to school was often delayed as the five year old stopped to watch the big boys throwing sticks up at the branches in their impatience to make them fall off. Then she would hear the 'warning bell' and run fast before the second one sounded to say it was time to go in, and then tag on the end of the queue of children, usually just in time to march into the classroom under the stern gaze of the duty teacher.

Joan's teacher was Mrs. Owlet, a plump lady who suffered no nonsense from any of the forty or so little boys and girls in her class. Every child knew they had to sit quietly as she told them the familiar Bible Stories and reminded them of the Ten Commandments, which they had to chant out loud. Not that anyone understood all of them.

"You can understand the main ones," she said, unabashed by the blank faces staring back at her.

"You all know what 'Thou shalt not steal' means' and 'Thou shalt not kill'. You'll learn what the rest mean when you get bigger."

Mrs. Owlet was also the head teacher and if anyone did try to disturb her when she was in 'full flow' they were soon told to stand in a corner with their face to the wall. In this way the children learned quickly and most of them could read and do simple sums.

They had progressed beyond the Little Black Sambo books which were just for the 'babies', and now they were reading the 'Just So' stories by Rudyard Kipling, all about how the 'leopard got his spots', or how the 'lion got his roar'.

She made a new friend called Margaret and it didn't take them long to discover that the railings around the school playground were just exactly the right width and height for a small child to swing their legs over and dangle upside down innocently displaying their green school knickers to the passers-by. Dangling in this position, with their skirts completely covering their faces, the girls would have deep and meaningful conversations, at playtime, with whosoever had decided to swing their legs over the railings at the side of them.

Margaret was very impressed that Joan lived in a train carriage.

"Did you go to the seaside in it?" she said from underneath her skirt as she swung her legs over the railings.

"No – don't be so silly. If we did that then all the furniture would fall over, we went to the seaside in a proper train. And…" Joan said, as an afterthought, "I had rock *and* ice cream and the rock had letters going all the way through it!"

"I had an ice cream too!" said Margaret from beneath the folds of her skirt.

Two black pigtails dangled above the ground with about half an inch to spare. "Can I come and see your train carriage?"

"Yes if you want, we shall ask your mummy when she comes to meet you."

"I have a swing too!" boasted Joan to whoever wanted to listen, "My daddy made it and it is bigger than any in the park."

"You *are* lucky!" There was a different voice from further along the railing, "I don't have a daddy to make me a swing!"

Joan risked life and limb by taking one hand off the railing to lift her skirt away from her face, precariously dangling by her legs and one hand. It was hard to tell who it was behind the folds of pleats but the ginger hair just brushing the ground gave away that it was possibly Joyce Brock.

"My daddy never came home from the fighting!" the voice went on. "Mummy says he is in a foreign field."

Joan didn't know what a 'foreign field' was but her legs were starting to ache so she carefully unhooked them and allowed her feet, followed by her bottom, to land on the ground with a thump.

"I stayed up longer than you!" laughed Margaret jumping down and rubbing the backs of her legs.

"So did I!" said Joyce, who stayed where she was.

"Why was your daddy in a foreign field?" said Joan. She went over and lifted the skirt away from the upside-down face, confirming that it was, indeed, who she thought it was.

"He was fighting to stop the Nazi's," said Joyce and then he died and went to heaven and now he is in a foreign field."

The school bell put paid to any further conversation, but Joan thought that she might have to find out what a 'foreign field' was. Maybe it was where the 'bloomin eye-tyes grew and she had heard 'nasties' mentioned before somewhere!

"And," Joan continued, only half listening to Joyce, as they lined up to go back into class, "I have a playground that is as big as this one!" She waved her arm to encompass the whole of the school play area.

"Oh, I don't believe that" said Margaret who was standing in line behind her, "you are fibbing – show me then!"

Consequently Lily never knew, from one day to the next, who was going to turn up from school with her daughter. In fact, Margaret lived in completely the opposite direction from the school, so she had a very long walk home after a visit to No.2 Timber Site.

Nobody worried about their offspring though. There was no traffic to run them over, they were unlikely to get lost, and anybody crazy enough to harm a child was locked up. There was a new found freedom that had come at the end of the war with the lifting of the black-outs and the knowledge that there was not likely to be any enemy lurking in the hedgerows any more.

Lily's biggest headache was always the same one though – what to give them to eat? Sometimes Stan would call in and see his parents and then come back with a honeycomb from his dad's bees, but more often than not, it was spread on bread without any marge or butter. Stan's vegetables, planted as soon as they had arrived, were beginning to become useful, and then there were always eggs to fall back on.

Somehow she managed but she never did quite know how. The children had their dinners at school, but they always arrived home starving, as if they hadn't eaten for a month. The 'good-old standby' was bread and dripping if they had been lucky enough to have meat for their Sunday dinner.

It was quite common for Lily to stand for an hour in a queue just to get some sausage meat from Sainsbury's. Then she would mix it with rolled oats to eke it out.

Very occasionally, for a special treat, there was jelly but it meant using part of the sugar ration which was still only four ounces per person per week. Jellies were kept for birthdays and Christmas to have with ice cream bought back from the village wrapped heavily in newspaper to stop it from melting.

Somehow though, she was able to feed her family *and* any school friend that her daughter brought home for a ride on the swing, or a slide on a tin tray down the reservoir hills, or a play on the 'iron things'. What Lily could do with the most meagre of supplies was sometimes a miracle in itself.

Youngsters were blissfully unaware of the struggle that was going on in the background while the nation waited for manufacturing and shipping to get back to normal. To them this *was* normal, just as 'normal' as Lily thought her life was, a generation earlier.

Meanwhile Stan had a very long day. He was gone in the morning before his child got up, and rarely returned before she was ready for bed. Even now, she had really only known him as a permanent fixture in her life for little over a year. Before that he had been 'here, there and everywhere'

The routine at No. 2. Timber Site never varied though. The evening drew to a close with a bowl of bread and milk or bread with an Oxo cube in hot water, followed by the inevitable Cod Liver Oil and Malt – or, in young person's language, 'Codleroilamalt'.

Then, mother and daughter listened to 'Larry the Lamb' on the wireless until they could hear the sound of the lorry as it trundled in and Stan parked up in his usual spot.

"Here's dad coming." Lily said, before even Joan heard the engine. Then the door opened at the front and in he strode with a wide beaming smile on his face.

He was always closely followed by old Ginger, who knew the sound of the engine too and hoped that his lord and master had a tit-bit for him. If he missed the RAF Stan never showed it, although sometimes he outwardly wondered where the family would have ended up and whether he would have got his 'Warrant Officer' badges.

No matter how tired and cold he was he always found time to spend ten minutes with his daughter and tell her a story before she settled down for bed. He also had to reassure her that he was not going away again – at least not for more than a day or two anyway.

Sometimes there were stories from one of her books, but many times he, like Charles before him, had to make up something on the spur of the moment. Stan made up 'garden stories'.

"This is a story about all the creatures of the garden." he said one evening, when all he wanted was his dinner and to 'put his feet up,' "Once upon a time there were moles and rabbits living in the garden."

"Granddad had pesky moles in his garden once" said Joan solemnly, "and he had bloomin' eye-tyes as well, he said so."

"Did he now?" smiled Stan, "you mustn't say pesky, it's naughty."

"I can say bloomin' eye-tyes though can't I, because Granddad does?"

"Granddad says a lot of things that little girls shouldn't say," he replied, thinking to himself that his father had a lot to answer for and was a law unto himself.

"What are bloomin eye-tyes? I think they are weeds."

He felt it was too late and far too complicated to start explaining what they were, especially as the memory of them bombarding Malta was all too fresh in his mind.

"If you want them to be weeds – then that is what they are," said Stan, let's finish the story, if my dinner gets cold your mum will be after me!"

"What's a foreign field?" said Joan suddenly, forgetting about the story altogether. "Joyce said that *her* daddy was left behind in a foreign field."

"I expect Joyce's daddy died in the war in another country and they have left him where he was in the lovely green field."

"Why did they leave him though?"

"Well, you know how Granddad looks after Edie's garden because she died and went to heaven when she was a little girl?" He was doing his best!

"Well," Stan went on heroically, "lots and lots of people lost their lives in the War – much too many to bring back home and there wouldn't be enough room for them all to have a garden each. So, they are going to make some great big ones for them in a 'foreign field' and I expect Joyce's daddy has been left there to go to sleep with all his friends."

"I'm glad you were not left there in a foreign field!"

"So am I!" said Stan with feeling.

"What are 'nasties' then?" she persisted. "Joyce's daddy was fighting 'nasties'."

He was beginning to realise that she wasn't going to let it rest.

"Granddad said that 'nasties' was a very good word for them." she went on.

Stan smiled to himself. He could imagine his father could come out with some even better words!

"I think they may have meant Nazi's!" said Stan patiently. He really *did* want his dinner! "But Granddad is probably right, 'nasties' will do for now – you don't need to know about them."

"Why not?"

"Because they are in the past – forget about them and do your rainbows instead."

"Oi! come on you two" cried Lily from the next room at the same time rescuing her husband from further interrogation. "Your dinner is getting cold Stan."

He kissed the child goodnight and she turned over and settled down to sleep, feeling very grateful that her daddy did not end up in a 'foreign field' no matter how lovely it was. She didn't want him to be chased by 'nasties' either. Whatever *they* were they didn't sound very nice at all!

"Oh gawd!" exclaimed Stan as he settled down at the table, "talk about twenty questions – it was like being in front of the Gestapo."

"It's called 'being a daddy.'" laughed Lily.

❖ ❖ ❖

Towards the end of 1946 Joan and her new friend Margaret tasted their first bananas! Very few children knew what a banana was. They came under the heading of the many exotic fruits that had stopped being imported in favour of more important things.

Not that anyone in the family ever went short of fruit. Charles saw to that, and even Stan was growing his own apple trees and blackcurrant bushes. As for Lily, she delighted in picking the blackberries that grew in abundance across the reservoir hills and using them in pies.

Stan had a long working week but he always finished at midday on Saturdays and was just about to climb into the cab to drive back to Walton, when John, the foreman, shouted to him from the office.

"Stan!" he called "Look what I have got." He pointed to a box on the floor. "It's just fallen off the back of a lorry mate." he laughed. "Do you want a bunch for the family?"

Stan looked at the large box at the side of John's desk. He couldn't remember when he had last seen a banana and now here was a whole box full of them, and in the middle of winter too!

"They just had a shipload in down at the docks." explained John, "The foreman said I could have a box but they won't keep."

"I don't know what my daughter will make of this!" he smiled as he picked up a bunch. "She has never seen one before – in fact I don't think Lil' has either."

"Not many people have," replied John.

"Well thanks mate," laughed Stan inwardly deciding that the least he knew about where they came from the better!

He left John and, taking the bananas, climbed up into the cab of his lorry – within minutes he was driving away from the east end and the docks which were still littered with bombed out buildings and huge mounds of bricks and debris.

He passed scores of civilians and servicemen alike who were trying to create some sort of order out of the chaos. The clear up, after six years of war, was barely beginning.

Lily had sent her daughter off to collect manure in her seaside bucket and had placed it on the garden by the lupins ready for Stan to dig in for next year. Both she, and Kenny Cox from No.1 had this chore on a Saturday morning, and Sandy and Brandy just looked on with indifference. They were fed so much hay that their droppings were nothing more than dried balls, like potatoes, and you couldn't collect much with a child's bucket and spade anyway.

"Don't worry," Stan had said, "every little helps!"

The horses had no sooner 'done their duty' than it was transferred to either Stan's or Coxy's garden. The result was better flowers and vegetables and Lily was happy too, because there was rarely anything left for the children to tread in. There was method in their madness.

Another feature of Saturday morning was usually the arrival of Margaret to play on the swing or to go in the fields even though it was cold and the nights were drawing in.

Joan had just deposited her last bucket of manure onto the remains of the lupins when her friend arrived, having been walked half way there by her mother. She had a request to look for what wild flowers were left from the autumn. Sandy and Brandy looked on in the background, quite used to having their peace shattered by their squeals.

Experience told Lily what to expect and so she already had a jam jar at the ready and some paper so that Margaret could take her bunch home.

"Come on," she called eventually, "leave those poor horses in peace – they put up with something from you two."

She held the wire up that divided the field from the concrete area and let the children climb through. They were such docile animals – one swipe of their back leg could send both of them over at once but neither went anywhere near their nether-regions. They knew better! So did the horses who always ambled down to the far end of the field at their own pace when they had had enough of the childish attentions.

"Let's go on your swing!" cried Margaret as she ran off around the side of the train carriage leaving her flowers with Lily. "It's my turn to go first!"

"No it's my turn!"

Joan was never a match for Margaret when it came to running and so her friend arrived at the swing first. They were still arguing about whose turn it was when they heard the familiar sound of the lorry and the swing was forgotten for a moment as Stan strode towards them followed by Lily.

"Look what I've got!" he grinned holding the bunch of bananas high up in his hand, "Here you can have one each."

Lily looked on amused in the background as the little girls jumped up and down trying to reach the fruit as he waved it high above his head. He finally gave in and passed them one each and one to Lily.

"What is it?" said Margaret, "it looks funny!"

"It's a banana" laughed Stan, "and you eat it – it comes from a long way off across the sea."

Before he could tell them anything more, both the children had bitten into the fruit and straight through the skin.

"Yuk!" Joan grimaced "it's horrible – I'd rather have an ice cream!"

"No, look you have to peel the skin off from the top, you loopy thing!" he laughed, "like this – you've seen a picture in your book of the monkey holding a banana – remember?"

He took another banana and peeled the sections down revealing the fruit inside.

"Oh that's better!" said Margaret, "what a strange taste."

The children had never tasted anything like it before and they were not really sure whether they wanted to eat anything that monkeys ate. Lily was already deciding that she would make some custard and have them as a pudding. They were like gold-dust and she wasn't going to waste them. The skins would go on the compost heap.

Joan had already decided that she preferred 'diddy-dottems'!

The children were unfazed by most things and for the infants the war was becoming a distant memory already as they were introduced to each new thing that they had never had before. As well as bananas, there was their first orange, sparklers on bonfire night, ice-cream and real toys – even comics and proper chips from a chip shop.

However, adults and older children could hardly forget and they were reminded every day in the newspapers and wherever they went, especially Stan who daily saw the devastation over vast swathes of London and the big cities that he delivered his loads to.

Younger children rarely got to hear the news or see the papers. Both parents and schoolteachers alike, decided that what they 'didn't know wouldn't hurt them'! It wasn't easy to shield them completely though, as day after day there were more revelations and the grown-ups inevitably spoke amongst themselves and were overheard by prying ears.

Even Stan, who had been in the thick of it since the beginning, began to feel as though he knew nothing! He found himself reading about battles that he had been involved in and yet never knew the true extent of the casualties or the significance of them at the time. There were always pictures at the Cinema of the wrecking of the big cities, not just in England, but in so many parts of Europe.

Sometimes, when Stan had a particularly long journey to do for the haulage company, he stayed overnight 'in digs' in Manchester or Liverpool, and then come back the following day. On those occasions he went to the pictures with one of the other drivers, usually Bert. There he saw Pathe News and stared speechless at the panoramic views of Hiroshima and Nagasaki, simply wiped off the map, and the dreadful images of what went on in the German Concentration Camps. It was unbelievable and something that nobody could talk about.

The men just stared opened mouthed at what they saw until the original film that they went to see became of no consequence at all. Then there were the shocking pictures of Malta being bombed, and yet it still seemed like a bad dream to him and hard to believe that he had been underneath it all watching it. Even the hospital that he had finally been invalided to had received a direct hit soon after he had left it. Once again he wondered how many of his nine lives he had used while he was there.

When Joan was out of the way in bed, wireless documentary programmes gave even more information every evening and Lily and Stan listened with increasing speechless horror. It got turned off very quickly if she came through from the bedroom unexpectedly though.

Lily always tried to make sure that the very last thing that her daughter did before going to bed was a visit to the toilet, but just occasionally there became a need for her to run through the train carriage in her pyjamas.

"Sorry, I've got to go!" she cried as she ran crossed-legged in front of them.

There were many times when Stan nearly broke his neck turning the wireless off so that she did not hear the awful things that were being broadcast. He felt that young children should be protected from such things. Consequently, most children born at the beginning of the war grew up knowing very little about it.

"Oh it's not for little girls to know about," Stan always said when she asked. "You don't want to hear that stuff – it's Saturday tomorrow so you can stay up and listen to 'Educating Archie' instead.

She even tried to hear what they were listening to on the wireless through the wall, but the walls on a Pullman train were quite solid and the volume kept very low It didn't take her long to give up and go to sleep with the promise of being able to listen to 'Educating Archie' ringing in her ears!

Archie Andrews was a wooden ventriloquist's doll who, with his owner, Peter Brough, had his own programme on the wireless. The idea of it being strange to have a ventriloquist on the wireless did not enter the heads of either adults or children – it was their normality.

Occasionally Stan received letters from the very grateful French ladies whose lives he had most certainly saved. They had been little more than teenagers in 1940 when he had driven them away from the advancing Germans. Nearly seven years had passed and their letters told him first hand what it was like in their country now that they had got it back.

Once again he felt as though he was piecing together a huge jig-saw puzzle and he realised that it would be very many years before any of it made sense – if ever.

Not for the first time he thought of his father, and all his generation, going off in the 'first lot' – no wonder he didn't want to talk about it. He didn't either really – it was like a nightmare that held a morbid fascination but which you were glad not to dwell on for too long – and if 'Archie Andrews' succeeded in taking your mind of it, then he was worth the wireless time!

It was late autumn when Joan decided to collect the very last of the blackberries for Lily to make a tart. She had just arrived home from Sunday School where she had been learning about Moses in the Bull-rushes and how he grew up and went up the mountain and was given the Ten Commandments by God.

Nearly all the children went to Sunday School which took place in the Senior School – or the 'Big Boys School' as it was known – and she was no exception. The Ten Commandments were not only part of their learning at the infant school but the basis of their religious teaching and the construction to their daily lives. They were the laws and guidance that every child and most adults lived by.

Lily had made her a warm coat for the winter and a hat to match. It had been a job to get the material and had taken a lot of coupons. It was a pale blue with maroon trimmings and very smart. She was very proud of her creation, although she did make one glaring error. She gave the coat some big pockets, which seemed to be 'purpose-built' for hoarding conkers which by now were falling freely to the ground without the aid of sticks from the boys.

The children had collected them on the way home from Sunday School and Joan triumphantly emptied hers out on the dining table.

"Look what I collected!" she beamed.

"Oh you scallywag!" cried Lily in horror, "Look at what you have done to my lovely sewing – and get those darn things from off the dining room table – we are going to eat there in a minute."

She shook the coat outside until the dust and conkers cleared from the pockets and also rescued her daughter's best Sunday clothes from any further mishap.

"Go on with you, you go and get your old clothes on before you do any blackberrying – there won't be much left now anyway. They will all be finished."

Suitably chastised, the child ran through the train carriage to the bedroom and put on her old dress. She was much too big for her dungarees now.

"You'll have to have a 'hooky-stick'" said Stan as she came back, "Your mother's right though – they will be all over by now – come with me and I'll make you one, and then you can reach any still left at the back."

"Anything for a quiet life!" he thought.

"Don't be long," called Lily grumpily. "Dinner is nearly ready.

The two of them disappeared into the 'air-raid shelter' shed where Stan kept his motor bike. He scrabbled around at the end and emerged triumphantly with a long pole which he hammered a nail into to make a hook.

"There you are!" he smiled "a hooky stick, you can pull the bushes that are far away towards you with that hook, see – like this!"

He went outside and demonstrated by hooking at the last of the evening primroses growing at the side of the shed. She felt very important.

"Oh look!" she laughed, "I look like Moses – he had a stick like this to help him climb the mountain."

"Did he?" replied Stan, "What else did you learn about Moses?"

"He went up the mountain and God gave him the Ten Commandments." Stan passed her the stick.

"Can you remember what the Commandments were?" he said with a twinkle in his eye.

"Oh yes, we did them with Mrs. Owlet at school too. I only know three though. Thou shalt not kill, and thou shalt not steal and thou shalt not bear false witness – and false witness means telling fibs," she said all in one go without pausing for breath.

"There is another one" said Stan solemnly "thou shalt not put dirty conkers in your pockets!"

She gave him a withering look, picked up her jam jar and stick and walked towards the hills.

"Well you are not doing too bad!" called Stan after her, "If you remember those you will not go far wrong – I expect you will learn the rest one day."

He watched her as she strode off to the reservoir hills with her jam jar and her hooky stick, pretending to be Moses. She crossed the field and promised herself that she would get a lot of blackberries and some flowers to make up for the mess she had made of her mother's handiwork with the mucky conkers.

Sandy and Brandy looked on without moving a muscle. After all, they were used to the comings and goings of the children and they knew that she did not present any danger to them, other than pinching their poo when they were not looking. She marched across the little bridge over the stream pretending to be Moses. Then she peered down at the frogs and remembered about when she told Mrs. Gabriel that if you held them upside down their eyes would pop out! She was older and wiser now and realised that this was probably not true. It was just a story but she wondered if it counted as 'bearing false witness.' She decided that she might tell Mrs. Gabriel next time she saw her walking her bulldog George down the drive at Coxhill.

She poked the frogs with her stick and watched them hop away among the reeds as she imagined for a brief minute that there might be a basket in the bulrushes like the one that the Pharaoh's daughter found. Then she shook off the idea and used the hooky stick to climb the hill.

There were hundreds of blackberry bushes all around the reservoir, but she had strict instructions not to lose sight of the train carriage. She looked back and could see it in the distance and knew that one or other of her parents would be watching out. There was a likely bush just half way up the hill that she had her eye on and, with the stick she could reach right to the back.

She put her jar down behind her and reached across. There were a lot of cobwebs, all undisturbed.

"Ugh, I don't like spiders!" she said, to nobody in particular, and proceeded to use the stick to bash down on the webs. She had already forgotten about Moses or the commandment which said 'thou shalt not kill'! Suddenly the stick came down on a solid object with a loud cracking sound that made her jump.

"Whatever is that?" she thought. At first she thought it was a rock and nearly bashed it again, but instead she used the hooky stick to part the brambles only to reveal the barrel of a shotgun.

She knew just what a gun was. She had seen them before. She knew Granddad used one when he went to hunt for 'pies' because Auntie Rosa took a photograph of him with it, and Granddad Gosley had one that he kept locked up and used for shooting grouse and pheasants.

This one had a brown wooden base and brass bits on it and really looked very big lying there in the blackberry bush.

The hooky stick was well and truly stuck in the brambles and she could not move it. If she struggled too much then it might fall further into the bushes, and she didn't want the gun to go 'bang'! More importantly, she did not want to confront any more horrible spiders! She didn't want to lose her precious stick either.

It was quite a dilemma but eventually she decided that there would be no choice but to let go of it. She put it down gently and ran back down the hill and across the little bridge to the train carriage, leaving her jam jar on the grass.

"Dad, Dad!" she shouted, unaware that she was frightening the horses, "I've lost my hooky stick, and" ... it was almost an afterthought and not nearly so important, "I found a gun!"

The horses ran off down to the end of the field as she crawled under the wire.

"Mum, Dad!"

They both came running out.

"Show me!" said Stan briskly.

"Are you sure it was a gun?" said Lily "it might have been just a stick."

"No, it was a gun, come and see, but I lost my hooky stick too!" She was off again running ahead as Stan strode off behind her.

Lily stayed at the door and watched them as they crossed the field, perfectly convinced that her daughter's vivid imagination had run away with her. She was still a bit annoyed about the conkers and she had some lamb ready to dish up for dinner. She had queued for it for much longer than a pregnant lady should·be expected to do.

Stan followed his daughter and looked at where she was pointing, blackberries totally forgotten. It certainly was a gun – and a lethal looking weapon too. Lord knows where it had come from but he knew it wasn't British. He looked up into the empty sky. Maybe a parachutist had dropped it on his way down – it could have lain there undisturbed for a couple of years. He grinned inwardly to himself – it could have been one of his father's 'pies',

"Stand back!" he said sharply. "Go over there, right out of the way!"

She did as she was told as Stan pulled the bushes back and gently eased the hooky stick away from the trigger. Then he leaned over and grabbed the handle, carefully keeping the barrel pointing at the ground and as far away from himself as possible. He quickly noticed that it was fully loaded.

"Go back to your mother!" he shouted, "Go on – go back out of the way!"

She ran off carrying the precious hooky-stick while Stan gently eased the gun out from where it had lain undisturbed until now.

"Was it a gun?" called Lily, as Stan carried it carefully towards the air raid shelter.

"Yes, stay away Lil'" he replied. "Keep her indoors until I have locked it up."

He carefully placed it in the old air raid shelter.

"It can go in there until the police turn up for it!" he stated as he picked the gun up and placed it on the floor of the lock up. He turned the key and came into the carriage.

"Whew!" he sighed, "I'll have to call the police, they might be looking for this – it is certainly not a toy – you never know when a gun has been laying unattended – anything can make it go off."

The company phone had been left behind. It seemed to make more sense to leave it where it was than go through all the hassle of removing it. It would just be there to connect to the London office or for the emergency services. This was an emergency!

He phoned the police and then Lily gratefully got on with dishing up the dinner.

"Come on, it will be a burnt offering soon," she said "don't forget, I'm feeding for two and we are both hungry!"

They had barely finished their pudding when there was a screech of brakes and a jeep pulled up outside carrying an American Army sergeant and a police constable.

"There will be a reward for this young lady" said the sergeant as Stan handed him the gun, "it's a good job you went back and told your daddy – it could have blown your head off!"

"All right, that will do!" said Stan, "we won't have that sort of talk in front of the child."

"Sorry." said the sergeant politely, "I bet it was dropped by some kraut spy –it's not the only one we have found – most of 'em ended up over at a camp at Richmond.

He emptied the bullets out and put it in the back of his jeep as he spoke.

"What's a krows pie?" whispered Joan.

"A bit like the nasties." giggled Stan as the visitors waved goodbye and drove out onto the road, "only they are gone for ever."

"Hopefully!" finished Lily.

A week later the sergeant came to the door carrying a large box and inside was a real dolly. Not a knitted dolly or one made with paper, but a *real* one with golden hair, and if you squeezed its tummy it said 'Mama' and it had come from

America. Very few in Joan's class had real dollies unless they had been lucky enough to have parents or grandparents that might have owned one in the thirties. She was overjoyed and couldn't wait to get back to school and tell everyone. She had never seen one like it before. As it happened, neither had Lily!

She would have to have a pram or a cradle, and as you could not buy these things it would have to be made. Stan gave it immediate thought and decided that it was easier to make a cradle for the doll than a pram. It would be his next project in time for Christmas. He briefly wondered if he was likely to have enough hours in the day.

The gun was yet another reminder, as if one was needed, of how close we came to being invaded. In fact, as each day went by and events were pieced together, Stan could quite often be heard muttering under his breath to himself – "we never knew how close we came…" and every day, like Lily, he counted his blessings.

14. *"All in all 1947 was a turning point for everyone…"*

The phrase 'foreign field' cropped up again in November. It was getting a bit too cold to hang from the railings and so most of playtime was taken up with running around to keep warm. Then Mrs. Owlet marched everyone indoors to have a bottle of milk.

"Come on everybody," sang out the teacher merrily, "time to get back to lessons, go and sit quietly at your tables, we will be doing something different today."

The milk was horrible because it had been warmed on the radiator but they had no choice but to drink it all up before going back to their desks and wait for whatever Mrs. Owlet had up her sleeve. She pointed to the big clock on the wall. The little hand was pointing to the eleven and the big hand to the nine.

"See," she went on, "it is quarter to eleven, and today is the day when we remember all those who fell in a foreign field". Ignoring the blank faces she carried on her speech.

"In a moment you will hear the school bell ring and when you do I want you to all stand up nicely and follow me to the school hall – do you think you can all do that?"

"Yes Mrs. Owlet," everyone chanted.

This was something that they had not done before, and sure enough she had hardly finished speaking when the bell rang out and there was the sound of doors opening and the patter of two hundred pairs of small feet hurrying down the corridor to the school hall. Everyone rushed in and sat cross legged on the floor with the teachers all around the sides to keep an eye on their charges. Mrs. Owlet climbed up on the stage and clapped her hands twice. It was enough. Two hundred children sat comparatively quietly and paid attention.

“Today children,” she explained, “it is the eleventh day of the eleventh month and soon it will be eleven o’clock. This is the day when we stand in silence and remember all those who are in a foreign field and who will *never* come home.”

One of the teachers looked at her watch and rushed to switch on the school wireless which was connected to speakers.

“In a moment children,” went on the head, “you will hear the sounds of Big Ben chiming the hour – when you do then you must stand up and be silent, like little mice,”

Everyone was too much in awe to make a noise or to not do what she said. It was such an event. There was a crackling and a spluttering from the wireless and then the unmistakeable sound of Big Ben. It was unbelievable – Big Ben in their school hall! In fact one or two of the children were too shocked to stand up and by the time they managed it the two minutes silence was half over! Nevertheless, considering no child in the hall was over the age of seven, it was a credit to the teachers. By the time it got to the second minute you could hear a pin drop.

“Thank you everyone” said Mrs. Owlet, “Well done – now let us pray.” Everyone closed their eyes and put their hands together.

“We pray for all those left behind in a foreign field, and say thank you for all the soldiers, sailors and airmen who saved us and brought us safely through the war.”

Joan noticed that many of the children, including Joyce Brock had a special place at the front of the hall under the steady gaze of the teachers, and once again she felt very pleased that *her* daddy was not left in a foreign field.

“Now children, I want you all to join in with me and sing the National Anthem, I think most of you know it right through by now, and I want you to sing it so that everyone walking down the street and in the houses nearby can hear you.”

She clapped her hands again, “Teachers, open all the windows if you please.”

They ran round and did what she asked and the icy wind came through the hall as Miss Lewis, the music teacher played the familiar notes on the piano.

It probably wasn't the best rendering of "God Save our Gracious King" that anybody had ever heard, or the most accurate, but it was certainly the most fervent and loud and George the Sixth would have been very impressed indeed with the sincerity shown by children and teachers alike.

Then, as a reward, every child was given a cloth poppy to take home with them.

Joan was quite worried about the festive season. After all, how would Father Christmas find her now that they were not at Granddad and Granny's any more. Stan was busy every spare moment in cleaning out and decorating the guards van for her bedroom. He made a good job of it too, clearing the walls and putting up cupboards he had made himself. Lily made pink curtains for the window and bought a pink candlewick bedspread to go on the camp bed when it was moved from the corner in their room.

Then there was also the little matter of the dolls cradle to make and to keep hidden. There barely seemed to be enough hours in the day, especially as everything had to be done in secret.

It was still a bit of a worry for a young child who lived in the guard's van of a train carriage which did not have a proper chimney.

"This is all very well Mummy!" said Joan one day, "but how will Father Christmas know where I am if I am in a new bedroom and not at Granny and Granddad's anymore?"

"We'll leave him a note," said Lily quickly.

This only satisfied her for a short while, until she had another, much more serious thought to consider.

"How will he get down our chimney?"

Quick thinking was required.

"Father Christmas is very clever," said Lily, "he'll come through the door!"

With her queries answered, for the time being at least, the child ran off outside to make a snowman.

She needn't have worried. Despite the acute rationing and lack of money, Lily and Stan did their daughter proud on this last occasion of her being an 'only child' and their first time as a family in their own home. By Christmas Eve she was in her own room with a stocking hopefully placed at the end of the bed.

"You *will* remember to leave the door unlocked for him?" she said, as Lily tucked her into bed.

"Yes, and we will leave yours open as well," smiled Lily "then he won't miss you."

She knew that the sliding door being pulled back would wake the child up and she did not want that!

Stan poked his head round the door. He was anxious for her to go off to sleep as 'Santa' had work to do. His feet hadn't touched the ground over the past couple of months, and to crown it all the weather was worsening.

"You listen for Santa's sleigh," he said, "listen hard and you will hear the bells."

She lay in bed singing 'Away in a Manger' to try to keep awake, but it was a lost cause.

Her life was far too active to remain awake for long and as soon as the singing trailed away her parents began their own brand of magic.

Stan brought in a fir tree from where he had been hiding it in the air raid shelter and Lily produced a box of decorations out of nowhere and started sorting them out. Within no time the living area of the train carriage had been transformed into a wonderland, which, considering their lack of funds and the austerity of 1946, was bordering on miraculous.

Then they bought in the doll's cradle from the air raid shelter where it had been hidden away and struggled with it into the bedroom, all the time trying not to giggle and wake her up

All that remained now was to creep in and swap a ready filled stocking with the one that lay on the bed exactly as they had done last year when they had been with Charles and Alice, and then carefully close the door. It all seemed simple enough, but it was hard to do it without laughing as they tripped over things in the dark.

Once they were contented with their efforts they settled down in their armchairs in the seasonal atmosphere of the decorated living room and listened to the carols on the wireless. They didn't have long though! Their daughter was asleep now but they knew that she would be awake bright and early in the morning.

Never before had Lily counted her blessings as much as she did on the night of the 24th December 1946. The weather and rationing could do its worst! She did not care one jot!

She got up and went into the little kitchen to make the cocoa, a drink that was still a luxury.

"Do you know what I would really like for Christmas Stan?" she smiled as she came out carrying the tray, "to know why your father calls your mother Kate!"

"It's niggling you isn't it Lil'?" he laughed, "perhaps he just likes the name Kate better than Alice, you know what he is like."

"I'd love to know though," persisted Lily.

"Anyway, here's to us!" said Stan, holding his cup in the air, "and here's to my father's son!"

It seemed that they had not been in bed five minutes before the sliding door between theirs and Joan's room thudded open and she came running through to inform them that he had been!

"He's been, he's been!" she shouted "Look!" She held the unopened stocking high in the air and then jumped on their bed.

"Mind, I've got a baby in there!" cried Lily, trying to protect herself from her noisy child.

"And he has left me a dollies cradle!" she shouted excitedly, totally ignoring her mother's protests. "Come and look, come and look – no – I must go out the back first."

She ran through the train carriage to the front, crossing her legs as she went, as Lily and Stan roared with laughter. In a few seconds she returned pulling at the bedclothes. Clearly she had totally missed the decorations that they had so lovingly put up in her efforts to get there and back in the quickest possible time!

"No peace for the wicked!" muttered Lily, as she crawled out of bed to save herself and the baby any further injury.

"And you Dad, come and see!"

They were not going to get away with it. There would be no rest until they had seen the cradle that Stan had made.

"Joyce said he wouldn't find me, but he has!" she cried.

He put his arm around his daughter.

"He will always find you my dear!" he said gently.

"Did you see the decorations through the front?" said Lily, knowing that her daughter had run right through the carriage with her head down concentrating on not wetting her pyjamas and had run just as quickly back in the morning gloom.

She didn't know which way to turn but pulled herself up short and ran back into the living area – stopping in her tracks at the door as she looked up and Lily put the light on. How could she have missed that?

"Oh look, he has put decorations up too – he must have fairies to help him – he couldn't do it all on his own." She stopped for a minute and looked round and then agreed with herself, "No, he couldn't do it all on his own – there must have been fairies."

The holly that Stan had collected from the common was all around the carriage, some at the top of every window with silver stuff hanging from it, and there was a beautiful Christmas tree and it even had coloured lights on it which he had bought in London. She gasped as her father came through and switched them on She had never seen a tree with lights on it before. They lit up and were red, green, white and yellow and it looked like fairyland.

The ever practical Lily left the two of them admiring the decorations and walked through the carriage to see if the chickens had laid – they still had to eat!

❖ ❖ ❖

The winter of 1946/47 seemed to go on forever. There was snow at Christmas and yet it was still hanging about as late as

Easter. It developed rapidly into a 'crisis' as, on top of the stringent rationing, the coal for the power stations could not be transported by road and rail. Most of the roads were impassable and even Stan could not drive his lorry. He tried not to have a hankering for the RAF but it wasn't easy at this time. Life was very difficult indeed.

By February the electric was cut off completely and only switched on twice a day, and all the roads were in darkness. It was like the blackout once again. Even the wireless was suspended. There was no Third Programme – not that anybody listened to it that much anyway – and all radio ceased at 11 p.m. Also television was stopped, but as ordinary people had never heard of television it didn't matter too much about that either!

There was no coke for the stove to heat the train carriage and Stan spent much of his time collecting logs and chopping them up to get some warmth to go around the place. For about the only time in her life, Lily felt that her parents were in the best position. Henry and the boys would make sure they had plenty of wood, and her mother was used to cooking on the old kitchen range. Lily's electric cooker was no good without power.

Joan thought it was ever so exciting! You could put pennies on the inside of the train carriage window and melt the frost so that you could peer out as if they were binoculars. You had to be careful not to put your face actually on the glass though because then it temporarily stuck! There were icicles all around the roof of their home, making it look like Santa's grotto. Once it started to get dark, then you had to use candles for lighting and they were pushed into melted wax in a saucer.

Lily was very unimpressed by it all. It was not the sort of weather for a pregnant lady to be out and about in and she had no choice but to let her five and a half year old go to school on her own – which the five and a half year old did not mind at all!

Stan still had to get to work somehow and undertook the perilous journey every morning into London, picking up what bits of shopping he could on the way back. Doreen Cox was very good but there were times when Lily wondered how they were going to get through this awful winter.

Even Joan got the job of doing some of the shopping. Lily wrapped a half-crown up in a piece of paper with a shopping list on it and pushed it inside her mitten.

"Now don't you go and lose it," she said, "there is no more where that has come from."

What was a very adventurous time for the children was a nightmare for the adults. In fact it was so cold that at Margate, where they had been on holiday with Wilf and Edie, some of the sea froze over! Lily wondered how on earth her sister Phyllis would be coping in Canada in weather even worse than this. It didn't bear thinking about.

The fact that mummy had a baby in her tummy was amongst the unexplainable things just accepted by a small child. It was like Father Christmas knowing where the train carriage was and God being up in the sky. If Lily felt the strain of it all she rarely showed it and her ever-expanding waistline was well hidden beneath her baggy maternity smock so that the child hardly noticed that changes were afoot. By March the thaw began.

Lily and Stan's eldest got the first signs that her status as an only child was ending in the early hours of a spring morning, even before the birds were awake.

There was the sound of movement and voices and doors sliding open and shut. Then she heard her father's voice telling her to go back to sleep. The next thing she knew there was a most unusual occurrence indeed. Dad was getting her out of bed and getting her breakfast ready!

"Your mother has gone to have the new baby," he informed her, but these momentous words paled into insignificance with his next statement.

"I am going to take you in the lorry to stay with Granny and Granddad for a couple of days, how would you like that?"

Any questions that she might have been building up in her mind about storks and gooseberry bushes and how much did a baby cost, *all* went out of her head. After all she could go in the lorry and mummy had already packed her a bag. This was an adventure indeed and she needed no second telling.

Stan lifted his daughter high up onto the seat on the left hand side of the cab and took his place behind the wheel. The sooner he got her over to his parents the better. Then he could concentrate on the forthcoming new arrival. He put two huge pillows for her to sit on but, even so, she could only just see out of the window if she stretched up. She could also feel the warmth of the engine, which was inside the cab between the two of them and covered with blankets.

The idea that she was about to get a baby brother or sister was unimportant against the trip in the lorry and seeing her grandparents again and she could hardly contain her excitement.

April 1947 – Gardener's Cottage

"Oh aren't you growing tall Joannie!" said Alice as she hugged her to her pinny. They said this every time she visited.

"Look Charles, she is nearly as tall as me – look." She stood back to back with her granddaughter and it was almost true.

"That's not difficult Mum." laughed Stan, "anybody is nearly as tall as you!"

She was a diminutive little figure and Joan quite thought she was beginning to shrink.

"I'm six soon!" she said, as if they didn't know it.

Stan, anxious to get back to his wife and new baby, whatever it was, bid his parents and daughter a hasty goodbye and they waved to him until the lorry was out of sight down the bottom of the road. Charles had his 'shadow' back again, and he was not complaining.

"Is George still here?" said Joan. She had not forgotten Mrs. Gabriel's old bulldog.

"Yes, George is still here," said her Granddad, "he's getting old now Joannie – like me!"

As he spoke, he automatically put the wireless on ready for the news as Alice clattered the dishes in the sink and Rosa came in from the garden to see her niece.

"Ssh you women, the News is coming on."

It was a routine that had never changed and never would, but just for once it was good news.

"The engagement has been announced of HRH The Princess Elizabeth to Prince Philip Mountbatten. They are to be married in the autumn."

"Gawd bless her," smiled Charles.

It was lovely to go down the gardens again with Granddad. Lily had made her some new dungarees because the ones that she had once made out of Granddad's trousers were much too small now and had become 'dusters'. Granddad had also made her a small hoe by cutting down one of his old ones.

"There, you can do some hoeing for me!" he said pointing to the newly sprouting lettuces, "See, all round there – get those old weeds out and earn your keep!"

She was in her element with her own hoe and felt very important.

"What's this!?" said Mrs. Gabriel as she came out to the kitchen gardens with George. "Have I got a new worker in my garden – my oh my, hasn't she grown Ratcliff?"

Joan stopped her hoeing and suddenly remembered that she might have told Mrs. Gabriel a fib the last time she saw her.

"I don't think the eyes pop out of frogs when they are held upside down." she suddenly announced. "I think that was a false witness."

"Was it now?" smiled the old lady.

"Yes!" She stood her ground, "One of the big girls told me, but it is a fib I think, and Moses said that you must not tell false witnesses."

Mrs. Gabriel and Charles tried hard to hide their smiles.

"Don't worry Joannie!" she said "I am sure it was just a little fib, and you have done such a good job of the hoeing."

Charles couldn't help but think that Mrs. Gabriel was telling a bit of a 'false witness' too!

One of the first things Joan did when they got back from the gardens was to go and have a look under their bed for the 'Gazunder'.

"Oh it's gone," she said to Alice, "the Gazunder has gone.!"

"You haven't looked very hard," laughed her grandmother, "you have just walked right past it, come and see!" She followed Alice out to the back door and looked up to where she was pointing.

"Your Granddad thought that it would be of better use there!" she smiled.

He had drilled the Home Guard helmet with holes and planted it out with pansies and there it was, hanging above the door. Charles Ratcliff was never a person to waste *anything*. Joan was very impressed but there was much to do and to check up on, so it wasn't long before she inspected the chickens and the rest of the garden that she hadn't seen on the previous day.

The one thing that Granddad had not removed was the painting of the rainbow. It had been on the mantelpiece for over a year now and was looking the worse for wear and all the colour had faded from it. It was little more than a blob.

"I'll do you a better rainbow soon Granddad," she said.

"You can if you like, but I shall still keep this one," he grunted. He was an old 'softie' underneath his gruffness – just like the grandfather in 'Heidi', a book that Father Christmas had brought her.

Stan arrived to collect his daughter when she was in the back field making a daisy chain. Despite the snow hanging about, she had found enough flowers to make the longest of daisy chains and now she would have to stop and go back home. She was not best pleased! Not that she minded going home. She loved the train carriage, even in the winter, but she loved her time with her grandparents too and it was an especially long necklace that she had made and her first of the spring. She was, therefore, a bit unhappy about leaving it, though she knew the daisies would not last long out of water.

"Come on!" said Stan "You have a new baby brother to meet."

"A baby brother!" squealed Alice, "Oh how lovely Joannie, aren't you a lucky girl?"

"Well done my boy!" Charles gave his son a hug and shook his hand.

"We are calling him Michael John," said Stan, "Lil' likes the name Michael and we thought of John after your father Dad." Charles was thrilled

Joan had never known her great grandfather John Ratcliff, who had died just a few years before she was born, but she had seen a picture of him, and he looked like a very kind man, just like her Granddad and her father. They all had the same kind blue eyes.

Of course the picture of the oldest man was in black and white but you could see that his eyes were light and Granddad told her it was because they were blue like his. After all, he should know.

"Come on Joannie!" called Alice, "Let's go and see if we can find some bluebells for you to take home to mummy and the new baby and leave these men to chat."

The pair ran off with Alice laughing like a young girl.

"Talking of names," said Stan, when they had disappeared across the field. "Dad, put us all out of our misery for God's sake, – why do you call my mother Kate?"

"What's wrong with Kate?" he replied.

"Nothing, but it's not her name." persisted Stan.

"Oh, every bloomin parlour maid in Britain born at the time of your mother was called Alice," he grunted. "When I first met her there were about a dozen parlour maids working in the same establishment all called the same and her surname was Jones – how many Alice Jones do you think there were? It was very confusing. The only way you could get to meet them was to send in a note with someone and you could bet your life they would always give it to the wrong girl – we didn't have the luxury of telephones then you know my boy."

Stan laughed, trust his dad to take the easy way out and simply change her name.

"Didn't her parents mind?

"Didn't ask 'em," he grinned. Then he caught sight of the intrepid 'bluebell pickers' coming across the field through the open back door.

"Does she *look* like an Alice?" he added nodding in their direction, "Of course she doesn't, she looks like a Kate!"

Stan looked up as the oldest and youngest women in his life approached the house, their arms full of bluebells and he had to agree with Charles. She did not look like an Alice.

That name conjured up a vision of neatness and primness like 'Alice in Wonderland'. The vision coming towards them was nothing like that! Her black hair, which was normally kept in rolls of curls around her head, had come loose and half of it was hanging over her shoulders. Her face was flushed and she was grinning from ear to ear. Her long purple dress with the little white flowers on it was looking dishevelled as if she had just been pulled through a hedge backwards – which, of course, she probably had.

"We had a bit of trouble reaching these ones!" she laughed, "but we got them in the end didn't we Joannie dear?"

She was nearly seventy now, but it didn't take much for Stan to understand how beautiful she must have been when his dad decided to call her Kate. She suited the name.

Just before they were due to leave Charles went outside and came back carrying a spiky looking thing wrapped in a sack. It was a small rose bush.

"Old Gabriel got these!" said Charles, "This one is for you Stan, I'm sure you can find a spot for it my boy, – it's called 'Peace'."

"Oh thanks Dad!" he replied, "I'll find a place for it, don't you worry about that!"

"It was cultivated just before the war," went on Charles, "but they hadn't named it – until now." Mr. Gabriel got them from somewhere and you and I have one each and there is one for Doris."

"Lily will love this."

Joan just thought it was a spiky looking thing in a sack, until her Granddad showed her a picture of it in a magazine.

"Here you are – this is what it will look like in a few months." It was a lovely picture of a pale cream coloured rose with pink edges.

"Put plenty of horse dung underneath it my boy, and it will win prizes!"

"Trust him to lower the tone," giggled Alice.

Joan couldn't help thinking that mummy would like the bluebells just as much.

It was time to go. Alice put the usual little packet of pear drops in her granddaughter's hand and gave her a hug, and Charles gave Stan a large honeycomb.

"There you are my boy – that's for Lily!"

They both hugged their son and granddaughter and stood at the gate as Stan lifted the child up into the lorry.

"We'll bring the new baby to see you just as soon as the weather improves!" shouted Stan.

Alice and Charles watched as the lorry disappeared down the road. Just for once Alice did not need to bury her face in her pinny and Charles did not have to bite his 'stiff upper lip.' It was such a short time ago when nobody knew what the future held. Now, the future held nothing but promise – and another grandson. They were both contented.

"Come on Kate," said Charles, "put the kettle on woman, and let's have another cup of tea."

April 1947 – No.2. Timber Site

Joan sat by the side of Stan in the cab and sang 'Away in a Manger' about twenty times, with the sound of the engine as background, before progressing to "Run Rabbit Run". By the time they arrived at No.2 Timber Site he had just about heard all her repertoire of songs. He lifted her down from the cab and she ran up the steps of the carriage and slid open the inner door to find her mother and the new baby.

"Look what I brought you." She held up the wilting bunch of bluebells. "You will have to put them in water – Granny fell in the bushes to get them for you."

The fact that there were probably just as many bluebells in between the reservoir hills was unimportant. It was the thought that counted.

Lily had been taught by her mother-in-law well. She immediately put the baby in his crib and went to get a jar for the flowers. There was the familiar smell of soap and lavender as she put her arms around her firstborn and introduced her to her new brother who was wrapped in a white shawl and sound asleep.

He was so tiny. Her dolly that she got for finding the gun was much bigger than him *and* it said Mama. But her mind soon turned to other things. Like, "was the swing still there?" and "are the horses all' right?" and "have the chickens been fed properly?" The whys and wherefores of his arrival were singularly unimportant to her young mind.

It was the Easter holidays and there was much to do. There were no chocolate Easter Eggs, but that was normal so nobody of Joan's age missed what they had never had. There would, however, be chicken's eggs painted with red cochineal and their *might* be a bar of chocolate and then, of course, there was always the pear drops.

She left Lily and Stan with Michael John, who at this stage, was not very interesting, and ran off across the fields of primroses to the reservoir hills. Just over a week ago they had been covered with snow – now they were awash with golden coltsfoot. The little stream was full of frogspawn just begging to be put in a jar, and there were irises growing up its banks.

The child ran up the hill trying, and failing, to avoid standing on the millions of coltsfoot and stood at the top, looking down on her train carriage home. There were still a few patches of snow in the shaded areas, looking quite strange, considering the wealth and abundance of flowers about the place. Even the blackberry bushes were coming into bud with promises of the white flowers that would inevitably form.

She looked at the bank stretching gently down from where she was standing and made a mental note that it would be good to slide down there on a tray again. When she got back to school she would remember to remind Margaret about it.

Any talk of 'bloomin' eye-tyes' or 'nasties' had completely gone from her mind for the time being at least.

On the other side of the horse's field and dividing it from the road, were the long line of bushes covered in white May blossom. It looked like snow in itself.

She sat at her favourite spot and all around her the birds, totally unafraid, were busying themselves collecting straw and twigs for their nests and once or twice she spotted a rabbit scurrying to its hole in the side of the bank.

Suddenly she felt the spits and spots of rain coming out of an almost perfectly blue sky and the sudden rush as a group of blackbirds soared into the air from a nearby lilac bush. She jumped up and slid down the hill on her bottom, crossed the little bridge over the stream and ran across the field, just as a shower of rain came down from, what seemed like, nowhere! As she ran she could already smell the familiar aroma of wet grass and the scent of the flowers and blossom.

"Come on you silly girl!" called Lily when she got close. "What were you up there dreaming about – you're soaked." She grabbed a towel from the warm pipes and rubbed her hair dry immediately giving her daughter a sense of well-being.

"Look!" Stan suddenly cried, "Look over there!"

Lily looked out through the large window to where he was pointing and there, making a perfect arc across the hills, was a rainbow.

Both she and Joan ran outside, ignoring the wet and leaving baby Michael safely in the warmth of his crib. He was too small to go anywhere and was sound asleep all wrapped up in a tight shawl.

It was a beautiful rainbow and Joan had not forgotten the story of Noah as it was told by Granddad.

"See Mum!" she said, "Noah's rainbow!"

She was too young to remember *everything* about being evacuated although she did remember the cot in Newcastle very well and the Ovaltine tablets at Chippenham and Little Black Sambo. It was strange, because it seemed as though her dad had always been around but in fact it was still less than two years. For Lily and Stan though, the memory was all too clear, especially when they glanced up and could see the huge silver barrage balloon still hovering in the skies over nearby Kingston.

"Come on, we are all soaked again!" laughed Lily. Her mothering instincts quickly returned as she ushered both her husband and daughter indoors.

They dried themselves down and then for some time watched the rainbow through the window until it started to fade away as the rain died down and the atmosphere changed. Meanwhile, Michael John had slept through it all peacefully, unaware as to what he had missed.

That afternoon Stan planted the Peace rose by the front door of the train carriage according to Lily's instructions. She wanted it right by the steps so that she could see it every time she came in and out. He remembered what Charles had said and went and got a shovel full of manure to dig in with it.

"There, that should be O.K." he said to Lily, "Let's see if it is as good as dad says it is going to be."

"You can guarantee that he will soon tell you where you are going wrong next time he comes over." chuckled Lily.

Joan had a look at her father's handiwork with the rose. It still didn't look like much to her. Then she went indoors and found her drawing book and paints.

"Now what are you painting?" said Stan, as if he didn't know.

"Another rainbow" said Joan. "If a rainbow means that everything is going to be all right then we must have one for ourselves – and Granddad needs another one too and I may do one for Granny Gosley."

Lily thought her mother could do with a few rainbows!

Stan made a promise to himself that he would take his daughter to see the Wizard of Oz' when it came locally and his mind drifted back to that day in 1941 when he had been on guard in Malta and the bombs had been raining down in their hundreds from the sky without a single rainbow in sight.

As for the 'first lot' – on one of the rare occasions that his dad had, very briefly, spoken about it he had said, "Ah my boy – all I could hear from the muddy trenches was the Lord's

Prayer being said hundreds of times over and over again, by very, *very* frightened men."

He tried to push it from his mind but it was not to be – he picked up the daily paper and one particular news item caught his eye. The King had awarded the whole Island of Malta the George Cross for the way its people had defended it against the Germans.

"My goodness!" he said out loud, "look at that Lil' – they jolly well deserved that – they really did."

It was just a tiny little 'dot' in the middle of the Mediterranean but it had been so crucial to the War effort. It had sustained more consistent bombing than anywhere else in Europe. He had been in a different war to Charles, a different generation, but he had heard the Lords Prayer said a few times by frightened men too, especially in Malta.

Stan brought his mind back to the present day and looked across at Joan stirring her paint brush around in a jar of mucky grey looking water. Michael John was lying quietly in his crib whilst Lily sang softly to herself in the scullery. Perhaps it was at that moment that he stopped hankering for the RAF and the life he had left behind. Of course he would always get that automatic straightening of the back and the tingling down the spine whenever he heard the RAF Central Band play the 'General Salute' but he could live with that. It was called '**pride**'.

All in all 1947 was a turning point for everyone. Bombed out buildings were all over the place but foxgloves were starting to grow through the rubble now. People were living on spam, even horse flesh and squirrel in some parts of Britain but bit by bit things *were* improving and everyone helped each other by sharing their vegetables where possible. There was hardly any fuel and there were constant electricity cuts, but for all that, it was as if a burden had been lifted and people could look forward to building a future.

Of course, there were many children, who were still waiting in vain, for their fathers to come home, but those same children could play undisturbed in the fields and streets and walk great distances to school, generally, without mishap, and it so nearly did not happen. Edie and Wilf could vouch for that! People in 1947 were too grateful for what they *had* got than to moan, about what they hadn't got. Wages were poor but nobody 'wanted' anything or were jealous of anybody else.

Lily finished doing the dishes in the tiny kitchen which had once been the second toilet on the Pullman train. She thought of her mother who would be boiling up water on the kitchen range, or waiting for the horse and cart to come and empty the tin toilet, and counted her blessings again. She was even grateful to her father for sending her out into service now.

It was funny how things did seem to work out right in the end and how one split second decision in one generation marked the future for the next.

She looked at herself in Stan's tiny little shaving mirror and brushed back her dark hair from her face. Fortunately, she still only looked the 32 years of age that she was, although she felt as though so much had happened she really ought to be older!

In the main living area Stan was contentedly minding the children – an unusual sight as he rarely sat still for long. He was thrilled because he had just received a letter to say that his sister Doris had a little girl that she was calling Margaret. There was just two weeks between the two babies. Also there had been an Air Mail letter from Lily's sister in Canada to say there was a new niece there too – baby Linda had arrived. The next generation was emerging.

It was hard to believe that it was still less than ten years since match-making Doris had introduced Lily to her brother. What a handsome man he was! His lovely black hair was already going prematurely grey even though he was only 36 but it was still thick and wavy and complemented his kind blue eyes set in the brown weathered face. He was like his father and yet he had many of the qualities of the more gentle and refined Alice. Lily, like her daughter, was so very, very glad that he had not been left in a 'foreign field'.

Everything she had ever wanted was right here in this Pullman Train Carriage in the middle of, what used to be, a Timber Site, which in turn was in the middle of reservoirs.

❖ ❖ ❖

On Joan's sixth birthday they had a 'visitation'! It was from no less a personage than Henry Gosley himself! It was such an unusual occurrence that his granddaughter thought he was Winston Churchill which caused much laughter.

Until Michael was born Lily usually nipped to see her parents while Joan was at school – it was easier. Therefore it had been some considerable time since she had seen her other grandparents. In any case Henry was usually missing anyway, visiting the Sergeant's Mess at the Army Barracks where he still worked from time to time. However, the idea of his daughter living in a train carriage must have been too much for his curiosity. Not only that, his first grandson had arrived, so, without any warning, he arrived unannounced one Saturday morning, when Stan was at work, taking both his daughter and granddaughter totally by surprise. Michael was oblivious to this momentous event.

Lily was through the back of the train hanging out her washing when there was a knock at the front and it was Joan who ran to answer it. Framed in the doorway, with the light behind him, was a stocky figure in a black pin striped suit and trilby hat, smoking a cigar.

She immediately thought she was looking at the great man himself and didn't stay for a second glance to make sure! They had just been learning about Churchill at school. His picture was in her school books, on posters and on the front pages of all the newspapers even though he wasn't Prime Minister at the moment. It didn't seem to make much difference to how much he was still in the news though and he was held in high regard by everyone. On the other hand she had not seen Henry for months!

She stood stock still for a minute with her mouth wide open, looking at the figure with the portly belly and gold watch chain across his waistcoat. Then she slammed the door in his face and ran down through the carriage colliding with Lily on the way and waking her little brother up from his sleep.

"Mummy, Mummy – it's Mr. Churchill" she shouted, "Mr. Churchill is at the door – I know it's him – we did him at school with Mrs. Owlet!"

Henry pushed the front door open and strode through the carriage and gradually Joan realised her mistake as he and her mother dissolved into peals of laughter.

"Honestly" laughed Lily, "whatever makes you think that Mr. Churchill would want to come and see us?"

She looked at Henry. He had always looked like the great war leader but now he did so more than ever, and he played on it with the trilby and the cigar. Lily giggled to herself as she wondered what the people on the train would have made of him travelling third class in their compartment.

His first grandchild picked up the paper from the sideboard.

"Look Granddad" she said "You do look like him don't you – we saw him on big pictures at school too and you look just like him."

"I wish I had his money" laughed Henry as he took his hat off and sat down, puffing for breath, "well you have made your train carriage look nice Lily. "

He handed her a bag containing a rabbit he had shot all wrapped up in newspaper.

"It's a *coach* Father," replied Lily patiently as she put in on the draining board in the scullery.

Then she lifted Michael out of his cot to show him off to Henry. She didn't put him in the old man's arms though – she didn't fancy the tobacco from his smelly cigar clinging to the lovely white shawl. Besides, Henry did not 'do' babies – that was women's work. Of course this child wasn't carrying on the family name either – he would have to wait for one of his son's for that – but nevertheless he was still a grandson.

He settled down and enjoyed a cup of tea and some cake totally unaware that there was something very important that he had overlooked – much to Joan's disgust.

"It's my birthday today" she said pointedly.

Clearly he had forgotten and Lily hadn't reminded him. Generally speaking he was not a man who 'did' birthdays either. However, he dug around in his pocket and found a half crown. This was riches indeed – enough to by sweets for a couple of months, that is if you had the coupons!

"Don't spend it all at once," he said, "spend some and save some in your piggy bank."

Then he plonked his hat on his head, gave them all a quick peck on the cheek, and he was gone. Lily and Joan watched as he strode out along the road to the train station for the journey back to his old cottage that still did not boast a flush toilet and yet still looking, in one child's eyes anyway, like Winston Churchill.

Later that evening when Stan arrived in from work, Lily recounted the story to him.

"It's all very well though" he laughed, "it would have been all the same if you had been out shopping and then his journey would have been for nothing. I bet the old boy loved being mistaken for Churchill though."

"Well he does look like him," said Joan, "he does Dad!"

"Maybe Mr. Churchill's father had a bike!" chuckled Stan.

The remark went totally over her head and he was rewarded with a blank look.

"I wish I had a bike," she replied.

Soon after the visit from Henry, the peace and tranquillity was severely disrupted when Joan realised that Ginger had 'disappeared.' It seemed that with the arrival of Michael John the pussy cat vanished from the face of the earth! In fact he had 'met his maker'!

He was a very 'mangy moggy' and Coxy next door said that he was at least twelve years old, but he seemed to take a sudden liking to the baby's crib. Lily kept him shut outside but it was almost impossible to keep both ends of the train carriage firmly locked and bolted, especially when little girls were running in and out. She lost count of the number of times that she found him sniffing around the crib or, worse, trying to snuggle inside the blankets.

"Oi – you get out you mangy moggy" she would cry and then grab him by the scruff of the neck and place him unceremoniously outside the door. "It's no good – he is going to have to go"!

The summer months were approaching and Lily wanted to put the baby outside in his pram in the fresh air, but even with a net. Ginger still managed to get his own way. Finally and very reluctantly Stan took the old boy to the vet to have him put to sleep and it took Joan a few days to realise that he had, indeed, vanished.

Any hopes that Lily had that she would not notice soon disappeared.

"Where has Ginger gone? she cried, "I can't find him anywhere.".

Lily and Stan guiltily allowed their daughter to search all over the fields calling for the lost animal, until they could bear it no longer and felt they had to tell her the truth. They tossed a coin for who was going to do the sorry deed and it fell to Stan.

"Ginger has gone to pussy-cat heaven," he said solemnly, "he was an old mangy moggy and he had to go."

"Don't worry" he went on kindly, trying in vain to stop his daughter's tears, "I promise I will get you another pussy cat just as soon as your little brother is a bit older."

"How much older?" she grizzled, "it's all his fault anyway."

"No it's not," chipped in Lily, "he was an old pussy cat and he has gone to pussy cat heaven."

"I'll tell you what," said Stan sensing an opportunity for a bribe. "I will buy you some new paints to make up for it."

"We can't have mangy animals climbing all over the baby's crib," went on Lily, "you are a big girl now and you must understand that it is very dangerous."

She wasn't entirely convinced but realised that there was not much she could do about it and that was that – besides, new paints would be very welcome.

She grumpily picked up her drawing book and paints went back to her handiwork and put more birds in the sky and deliberately put an orange cat in the garden thus making Stan feel guiltier than ever. She made the wheels of her train carriage picture look like square bricks.

"Why are the wheels square?" said Stan as he leant over and looked at her painting, trying hard to ignore the orange cat.

"Well this train can't go anywhere – just like ours!" came the quick reply.

"Coach!" called Lily from the kitchen, "It's a *coach*!"

"Your mother is such a snob!" giggled Stan.

"Coach then." said Joan, "Our coach can't go anywhere and neither can this one and one day we will have another pussy cat won't we?"

"Yes, I promise."

She knew her father always kept his promises so that was sufficient to calm the situation for a while.

He got up and switched the wireless on as Lily came back in to put the tea on the table singing as she did so. It took a while to warm up but, when it did, Childrens' Hour with Uncle Mac' was just finishing. They were just in time to hear him say his immortal words ..... *"and Goodnight Children – everywhere"* Very gradually, oh so gradually, life was returning to normal. 'Normal' would do for him!! As for Joan – she was not quite old enough to count her blessings just yet, especially in view of the loss of Ginger.

By August the Peace rose by the front door was in full flower and no longer looked like a 'spiky thing'. In that same month Stan took his daughter to the pictures for the first time in her life. She saw 'The Wizard of Oz' and she heard Judy Garland sing 'Somewhere over the Rainbow.' It all seemed appropriate somehow. Well, Granddad had said that a rainbow meant that 'everything would be all right in the end' and he was never – *ever* wrong, was he?

One thing Granddad could not stop though was the 'march of time' and shortly after the arrival of baby Michael came news that Mr. Gabriel had died. Everyone, especially Charles, was genuinely very sorry indeed.

"He was a good boss," said Charles to Stan when the family went to Coxhill on a visit "the last of a very special breed – it's the end of an era my son."

Joan did not know what an 'era' was but she could see that Granddad and Granny were really quite upset. Both Charles and Christopher had been born into totally different classes but both respected each other. Even now, in 1947, Charles out of courtesy would touch his forelock when he greeted his employers and Alice had a job stopping herself from curtsying. In return they got loyalty, a roof over their heads and a happy and contented way of life.

"No" said Alice, "I really cannot complain about any of the gentry that I have worked for."

Charles shook his head again, "it's the end of an era Kate, the end of an era."

"*But then...*" thought Lily to herself, *"neither of them were scullery maids!"* Then she giggled at her own thoughts, Charles as a scullery maid would be an awesome sight!

15. *"When you open a door a window is bound to slam shut..."*

Four Years Later – Winter 1950 – No.2. Timber Site

The winter of 1950 had been nearly as harsh as that of 1947. There was thick snow on the ground and there were power cuts again. There was still rationing and you still needed coupons to go and buy sweets with your Saturday sixpence – not a lot had changed!

Four years on, and the train carriage remained an adventure for one who was not yet ten. At least, in the school holidays it did. However, it was a totally different story when term started and there was an hour and a half's walk in the sleet and snow to the big school which was much further away. Although most of the children were jealous of their classmate having such an unusual home, nobody envied her the trek, usually along dark unlit roads, which she had been forced to do since leaving the infant school two years ago. There was talk of a bus service to go her way but it had not happened yet and so there was no choice but to walk along the road carrying a bicycle lamp to see the way by. She did have her own bike now, but you had to be ten before you were allowed to ride one to the junior school and there were no exceptions. You were expected to walk as generations did before, and it didn't enter anyone's head that any child might be in danger.

She did have the company of friends for some of the way but, after that, all Lily could do was put Michael in the seat on the back of her bike and ride down the road to meet her eldest offspring, hoping, at the same time, that the children would not be dawdling. However, by the time the winter months arrived and, with them, the snow and slippery roads, Lily found herself to be pregnant again. Then, there was no choice but to leave the youngster to make her own way, sometimes not arriving in until long after dark.

On one infamous occasion she was 'kept in' after school for talking too much in lessons. This was no surprise to Lily but what *was* a surprise was that the teacher forgot her! She was eventually found by the caretaker, on her own, in an empty classroom. It was the final straw and an irate Lily did something unheard of – she called in at the school and gave the head teacher, all six foot four of him, a piece of her mind. Within a day, special permission was given for her daughter to ride her bike to school and that was that.

She also took the opportunity to call in at the Council Offices to 'chivvy them up' and to see where they were on the list. A new decade was about to start and it was time they had a house with a proper bathroom.

There had been little chance for the whole family to see the grandparents during this cold spell and Joan was old enough now to know perfectly well that it would be too much to drag her little brother over there on the train. Besides, she knew that her mother had another little baby in her tummy. She still wasn't sure how it got there though. There was talk of gooseberry bushes and storks again though she couldn't see the connection. There was a picture of a stork carrying a baby in it's beak in her old nursery rhyme book which had been passed on to her young brother, but she was beginning to doubt that story. After all, if it were true you would see storks flying around all over the place and you didn't.

"Don't be silly" said her friend Margaret from her upside down position with her feet against the school wall. "He's growing inside your mummy's tummy just the same as your brother did and your daddy put him there."

"How?" said Joan, as the school bell indicated that it was time to go indoors.

But Margaret was stumped on that one – she really wasn't sure and it was all far too complicated for anyone to bother about.

There were other things much more important for junior school children, like sliding on the snow and finding icicles and, just at this moment in time, getting into line ready to march into class without slipping on the icy playground.

Their teachers told them that they would 'learn about the birds and the bees' at the next school, when they were eleven, and that was all they needed to know for the time being.

"Time enough for you to learn about the facts of life then," said Mrs. Lane, their form teacher, "you concentrate on your sums and your spelling."

December 1950 – Gardener's Cottage

Now that she was older Joan could go with her father in the lorry more often and she did so just before Christmas in order to take presents around to the grandparents.

"Oh look" said Charles as he opened the door for them, "It's Santa Claus come to see us."

She went into the familiar old kitchen and was quite oblivious to the fact that her Granny looked decidedly frailer – something that had not been lost on Stan though. He knew the worry of having loved ones in two dreadful wars had left its mark on her as it had on the millions that had been forced to stay at home and wait.

His mother must have read his thoughts and looked ruefully in the mirror at the smattering of grey in her black locks and wondered at the 'blindness" of the young as Joannie jumped all over her as she always had done. She wished that she felt a bit better and could cope with it.

Stan suddenly realised that she had gone from being 'elderly' to being 'old'. He could remember her with long black flowing hair and running around like a young girl and it didn't seem like that long ago either. Then he caught sight of his own reflection. "*Mum's not the only one*" he thought "*mine is greyer than hers is – that's what the war has done for me!*"

Joan sat down at the table and Alice immediately put some hot toast and jam in front of her. The old rainbow picture was still tucked behind the pot of coloured spills that Granddad kept on the mantle shelf and she wondered just how long he was prepared to keep it there. She couldn't remember a time when it wasn't on show. It was a bit the worse for wear now though.

There was also talk of television. This was another of those things that she only half understood – a bit like only half understanding how Santa Claus managed to be everywhere at once and how God was up in the sky. Some children had talked about it in the playground but only one or two actually had one.

"Him and his old television" said Alice, "he is a one for his gadgets and it doesn't seem like five minutes ago since we had our first wireless."

"We have to move with the times Kate," he retorted. He looked across at Stan and answered the unspoken question.

"Got my insurance through son", he said "paid it in all my life – I might as well have something to show for it."

"I don't think Mrs. Gabriel has even got one yet" said Alice. To her it didn't seem right that they should have one before the 'gentry'.

"Dad's right Mum." Stan came to the defence of his father. "Just think how nice it would be to actually see Vera Lynn singing or see Max Miller telling his jokes."

However, the mention of Mrs. Gabriel caused him to automatically glance up at the clock and any further discussion was halted as he noticed the time. He had to get his load delivered and he wanted to get back to Lily. The new baby was due very shortly and that came before any more talk of televisions.

"Well, I am glad to see you have got your 'mate' with you son," said Charles nodding in Joan's direction as Stan pulled his coat on and made sure that she was properly buttoned up.

"It gives Lil' some rest," he replied, "and she keeps me entertained with her carol singing in the cab."

"Michael is not old enough to go in the lorry yet." Joan informed them, as if they didn't know.

Her grandmother put the usual little bag of sweets in the child's hand and Charles gave her a sixpence.

"Who knows Joannie," said Charles, who was really very excited at the prospect, "when you next come to see me you may be able to watch the television!"

"Huh!" grunted Alice, who really wasn't feeling at all well, "I'm told you have to sit in the dark – then Rosa and I won't be able to do our sewing."

The pair of them were still gently arguing with each other as they stood out on the pavement, like thousands of times before, and waved until the lorry was out of sight. For Alice, it was for the last time.

New Year 1950/51 – No.2 Timber Site

Richard Charles arrived at the end of December 1950, just before his big sister was due to go back to school for the new term. For the grown ups, the happiness at the arrival of the new baby was muted by the realisation that Stan's wages were going to have to stretch even further.

The struggle of the grown ups to make ends meet and the austerity of the time went right over the heads of the children. They were used to bread and dripping for tea and rabbit for Sunday dinner – it made two ounces of sweets once a week, provided you had the coupons, an especial treat but you never missed what you didn't know about and most people were in the same boat.

With Lily, as it turned out, only two days away from having the baby, Christmas was particularly difficult for everyone. However, Stan still decorated the train carriage and did his best to provide presents for the children and she tried to cook a nice dinner, which, to Joan's unbelievable dismay, included Genevieve! Jacqueline had already been 'done away with' the previous Easter while the child was at Sunday School. She learned later that her Dad had wrung the poor bird's neck and, like his father used to do before him, apologised all the time he was doing it!

She was not happy then and she certainly was not happy now.

"She's old now" said Stan as his daughter protested violently, "and lonely – poor old devil strutting around there all on her own."

She may have been old but she could still run and, despite the imminent arrival of the new baby, Lily laughed until she cried at his antics as he tried to grab the frightened chicken. Once he had wrestled with the bird in a rugby tackle and it was clear that it had given up the fight, Lily ushered the children out of the way while Stan did the deed.

"This bird will be as tough as old boots," said Lily later, as she had the unenviable job of plucking, pulling and trussing it.

In fact the only person to sit and eat the meat in the end was Michael. Lily just toyed with it, Stan had spam and Joan wouldn't eat it on principle.

The atmosphere improved when Joan discovered that there was a very large food parcel from Auntie Phyllis and Uncle Albert in Canada which contained sweets and goodies unavailable in England, not to mention toys. Lily knew that things were not easy for her younger sister at all with the harsh Canadian winter and the poor wages so was particularly grateful that she had gone to so much trouble.

To receive such a parcel was exciting and it didn't take the children long to help their mother open it. There was a woolly jacket for the expected new baby, a teddy bear for Michael and a 'Wettums' doll for Joan. You could put water in the little baby bottle that fitted in the mouth of the doll and, as if by magic, it would come out the other end into the cotton nappy the toy was wearing. It was a wondrous thing from half way round the world and a distraction from the sad ending of the remaining chicken.

On Boxing Day, seemingly out of nowhere Auntie Rosa arrived and Lily was whisked away to the maternity hospital. Then, one day later, while Stan was at work, the new baby made his appearance. The first Joan knew about this momentous occasion was the phone ringing – an event in itself – and then her Aunt rushing through the carriage to tell her that she had a brother.

"Joannie, you have a new baby brother!"

"But I wanted a girl," she wailed.

"You can't decide," replied Rosa "You have to take what you are given."

Lily came home with the baby on the last day of December 1950. Joan thought it all seemed a bit like magic. One minute there was just her and Michael – now there was another baby and mummy back in charge as Dad took Auntie Rosa home. Then, as she looked at the little bundle in the crib even she was beginning to wonder where the time had gone since they had first arrived at the train carriage. The days of pulling black out curtains tightly together and wearing nasty smelly gas masks and the bars of an Infirmary cot were just a distant memory.

She even knew what 'nasties' were now, and 'pies'. but she wasn't sure about 'bloomin eye-tyes'. It just seemed to be a family joke that she was not part of and she had long since given up trying to find out.

"What do you think of your new baby brother then?" said Lily as she came out of the scullery after washing some nappies. One thing was for sure, she wasn't the centre of attention any more – now there were two babies to take her parent's time up.

"I wanted a sister" said her eldest child, a touch ungratefully,

"Well we have to be content with what we have got" Lily replied, "we can't send him back."

Joan didn't bother asking where he would be sent back to – she knew her mother wouldn't tell her anyway and she was still smarting about the chicken.

Michael was less ungrateful than his sister and stood at the side of the crib looking at this new addition in wonder. He had grown quickly and was now a reasonable playmate. No doubt this baby would grow and be more interesting soon. At the moment he was letting everyone know that he wanted his tea and was very noisy indeed.

She looked in the crib at the mop of black hair against the whiteness of the sheet and decided that he would have to 'do' despite the row he was making. It looked like she was going to be stuck with two brothers and that was that.

It still seemed a bit unfair though – one of each would have been much better and this one was much noisier than the last one.

"What about me?" said Lily as she picked Richard up ready for a feed. "I had five brothers."

"Yes but you did have two sisters too."

"Huh!" replied Lily, "not for long – by the time my little sister was old enough to play with me I was sent away, and the youngest one wasn't born until I had gone to be a scullery maid."

"What's a scullery maid?"

"Somebody who does washing up all day."

There was no answer to that! It was time to go and show the eldest of her two brothers how to make a snowman.

If you open a door a window is always sure to slam shut! One month and three days after Richard was born – Alice died. It was as if a light had gone out and for a while no amount of rainbows would lift the terrible gloom and it even overshadowed the excitement of the new baby. Everyone tried to put on brave faces for the children but it was very difficult. However, if the grownups cried they did so behind closed doors. Consequently it took Joan a while to grasp what had actually happened.

"Granny has gone to heaven" said Lily glumly trying hard to control her tears and knowing that it wouldn't really hit the child until she went on a visit and saw that Alice was not there.

Four year old Michael would be none the wiser anyway and Richard would never miss what he never had.

She was as dear to Lily as her own mother and, like Charles, had been a rock during the long years of the war when she had waited, often in vain, for some communication from Stan.

"Ah well" said Stan as his eyes misted up, "poor old mum – she never did get to see a television after all did she?"

"I don't think she would have minded," replied Lily philosophically, "she wasn't a one for gadgets."

Doreen Cox came in to look after the two eldest children while Lily and Stan went to the funeral taking Richard with them. Joan thought that was ever so odd for a start – taking the youngest and leaving her and Michael behind, especially as they both looked very sad and were all dressed in black. It was a very unusual occurrence and she didn't like it one bit.

"You behave yourself for Mrs. Cox now," said Stan, as he adjusted his black tie. "We have to go and see Granddad and you have to be a big grown up girl."

"But *I* want to see Granddad!" The last time she had been left with a baby-sitter had been when there were black outs and they lived far away in somebody else's house at the top of all those stairs. It was strange – the older she got the more she could remember it.

"You'll see him soon," said Lily soothingly. "You do your drawing and make another picture for him to put on his mantelpiece."

"Maybe he doesn't want my picture," sighed Joan mournfully as the tears welled up and realisation dawned, "because things are not all right anymore are they – Granny's gone to heaven like Mr. Gabriel and Ginger." She paused for a minute – "and the chickens."

"Oh, he'll always want your pictures," replied Stan. "Go on, do him a nice painting and put some bloomin' eye-tyes in the garden for him, we'll see it when we come back and then you can take it next time we visit."

"There's no such thing as bloomin' eye-tyes," grizzled Joan who really was not taking too kindly to being left behind at all – it wasn't fair – after all she was nearly ten now.

The boys at school spoke about 'eye-tyes' but she knew they were not flowers because they ran around the playground with their arms outstretched, pretending to be aeroplanes. She guessed eye-tyes were the enemy, like the 'jerry' or the 'krauts'. She also felt that she was much too big to have a baby sitter. It was the final insult when one month old Richard was going and she wasn't! In fact, as Lily was still feeding the baby herself they had no choice in the matter,

Stan looked at the clock. They only had half an hour before their train was due. He proceeded to draw a house with some flowers round the outside while Lily tucked the baby into the carry cot. It was far easier to carry that between them than to lug the great big pram onto the train.

"I've never seen flowers like that before," she complained as Doreen Cox arrived.

"Well, those are the last of the "bloomin' eye-tye ones" grinned Stan. "I think we had better call them roses or daisies from now on."

Michael allowed all the activity to go right over his head. He was sitting in the pedal car that Father Christmas had bought him and was in a world of his own. One month old Richard was the only child to attend the funeral.

Alice was buried in Chobham cemetery, not too far from Edie and Mr. Gabriel. Charles would diligently look after all three graves for the rest of his life.

March 1951 – Gardener's Cottage

It was two months after the funeral before the family were able to go on a visit again although Stan called in from time to time to reassure himself that his father was adjusting to a life without his Kate and to keep up to date with the news.

Although we were officially into the fifties, there were still many people who did not have the telephone, including Charles. As far as he was concerned a television came first!

Stan only ever used the phone in the train carriage to take calls from the London office or in dire emergency. Therefore everyone still communicated by letter. If the family were planning to visit then Lily would post a letter on Monday. Alice, and now Charles or Rosa, would receive it Tuesday, therefore giving plenty of time for preparation for the 'onslaught' that was to come.

Once the worst of the winter weather was over Lily wrote to Charles as usual and the whole family went on train and bus. It was not something that either parent was looking forward to. It was one thing to talk about Granny being in heaven but quite another for the children to actually see that she really was not in the house any more.

The strange sight of a tall pole with a wire H on the top of it at the side of the bungalow paled into insignificance as Joan took one look at Rosa in Alice's place in the kitchen. She burst into tears as she realised, finally, that Granny really was not coming back and she would not be making pastry with her ever again. Instead, she looked down at them from a photo on the mantelpiece and Rosa had put a ribbon round it and a posy of primroses beside it.

"There" she said to the photo as she adjusted the flowers in their pot, "your favourites Mum."

Stan hugged his father. The big pole outside had not been lost on him.

"You did it then!" he grinned.

"Shh!" hissed Charles "I have a surprise planned."

He nodded in the direction of the corner of the room where there was a box shaped object with a cloth over it and a vase of flowers on the top. Then he looked across at his still tearful granddaughter.

"Don't you worry Joannie, I'll be seeing her again one day and every time I look at your rainbow picture I shall think of her – she has gone on ahead, that's all – she was always in too much of a hurry anyway – I always told her that but would she listen? – no!"

"I've done another picture for you" said Joan through her tears as she handed him her latest creation.

Charles looked at her drawing and grinned. She had come a long way since those first splodges in the magic painting book – it felt like only yesterday.

"That's a lovely one," he told her. "You keep up the good work and you will be winning prizes soon my gal."

Then he picked up Michael and sat him on his knee – the child certainly was not the chatterbox that his sister had been at the same age. He sat there quietly and looked up into his Granddad's face.

"He has my father's eyes" he said wistfully. "Life goes on…"

One thing was certain and that was Charles' unshakeable belief that he would see his Kate again – it was only a matter of time. She would be waiting for him.

“And she had better keep the place tidy until I get there!” he grunted as he put Michael down on the floor.

“Dad!” said Lily and Rosa together.

Joan hadn’t quite worked out how it was possible. They did sing ‘There’s a friend for little children above the bright blue sky,’ at school and she had heard of Jacob’s ladder, but it was all too much to think about and didn’t sit well with the talk of flying saucers and things of the future that some of the boys spoke about in the school playground. However, if Granddad believed that Granny had just gone on ahead then it must be so. He was never wrong.

Lily sensed the desolation that the old man was feeling and picked the new baby up and plonked him in his arms as Michael found his cars and happily played on the floor with them.

“Here you are Dad,” she smiled, “have a cuddle of Richard Charles – I promise he has just been changed and… his second name is after you!” If she was curious about the covered up television she did not indicate that she was and played along with the obvious ‘secret’.

His large gardener’s hands almost covered the baby completely as he gingerly held him to his chest for a while. Then, slowly, a smile of pride lit his face up as he held him close and then put him down gently in Lily’s arms. He had the dark brown eyes and black hair of Alice.

“We’ll have the whole ‘set’ here soon,” said Rosa, “Doris and Harry are coming over.”

“Goodness, you will have a house full” replied Lily, cheered at the idea of seeing Doris again.

Stan found his mind drifting back as he looked at his father awkwardly handing the small child back to Lily – was it still only six years since the war? It hardly seemed possible.

Alice was the first of the four people, of the previous generation, who had so affected the lives of the next. All four, Lily’s parents and his own, had been born in the 1880’s when Queen Victoria reigned. What changes they had seen in their lives and what an influence they had, in their own, so different ways, on the generations to follow. His mother had been the cement that held the family together through very extraordinary times.

"Boat Race day today" said Charles suddenly and mysteriously.

Then the penny dropped with Stan. His father was planning to watch the University Boat Race on television! This was the surprise.

His thoughts were interrupted by a loud bang on the door and the sound of Doris's voice.

"Hello there, anybody at home?" she chirruped as she pushed it open closely followed by eight year old Roger and his little sister Margaret and Harry.

The kitchen seemed to almost burst at the seams as they all hugged each other and tried to find somewhere to sit while Rosa put the kettle on and laid the cups across the big wooden table where Alice always made her pastry.

"Here you are, I've bought some cake," said Doris. She had the habit of cheering up the most miserable of occasions. "My goodness Joannie – haven't you grown – and Michael dear, what a big boy you are now!"

She leaned over and peered at the new baby.

"He's got his father's hair Lil' but mum's eyes I think,"

"What's with the pole outside?" said Harry "don't say you have television Dad?"

He was answered by a scowl and a 'shhh!"

Margaret and Michael disappeared under the table with a plate of cake each while Roger showed his Uncle Stan his latest drawings of aeroplanes that he had brought with him. He was a good little artist for an eight year old and Stan always showed an interest in his nephew.

For all the efforts made by the grownups it was still strange without Granny and Joan found herself looking for her and expecting her to walk in through the kitchen door any minute. In the end, she finished her cake and decided to go outside.

"I'm just going to find some bluebells" she told everyone, "Granny likes bluebells best Auntie Rosa."

"A bit early for bluebells" replied Charles, "there are a few out there though if you look in the shady bits."

"Don't go too far," instructed Lily. She looked up at the leaden sky and noticed that there was a distinct increase in the wind. She didn't envy the crews in the Boat Race for the weather was really taking a turn for the worse.

"I'll just go to the Drive."

She wandered outside to cross the field of daisies and buttercups that she had crossed so many times before and went through the iron gate that had held such mystery for her when she was four. She found herself at the top of the Drive that eventually lead into the gardens of Coxhill Manor. She was old enough to go wherever she wanted to now and at least, if she were outside, she could pretend that Granny was indoors making pastry as usual, or outside with the washtub in the garden.

There were a few bluebells growing in the shady areas where Granddad said they would be and she picked a few. Then she heard the sound of footsteps on the gravel of the Drive.

She looked up just in time to see the familiar erect figure of Mrs. Gabriel walking towards her pushing a big shiny black pram. She was dressed in sombre black with the usual wide brimmed hat with a scarf tied round it to stop it blowing away in the wind. She quickened her step as the sky got greyer.

"Hello Joannie," she cried when she spotted her. "Why I hardly recognised you – you have grown." It seemed to be the 'chant' of every older person she met.

Mrs. Gabriel silently wondered where the years had gone.

Joan tried to peer into the pram and came face to face with a baby, big enough to sit up, all wrapped in white and with a woolly pixie hood around his head to protect him. He looked back at her and gave her the type of beaming gummy smile that only a one year old can do. Had she not felt so miserable she would have laughed with him.

"This is my grandson Peter" said the old lady answering the unspoken question. "I just thought I would bring him outside for some fresh air."

She didn't like to ask her where her bulldog George was just in case he had gone to heaven too. It dawned on her that heaven must be getting pretty crowded.

"I am going to get a new kitten soon," she volunteered, "and I think I might call him Peter if he is a boy one – I have a boy in my class called Peter too."

"That's nice" said Mrs Gabriel as she jiggled her grandson up and down in his pram causing the child to chuckle even more. "Did you hear that Peter? Isn't that nice?"

"And – I have got a new baby brother" Joan went on "his name is Richard Charles, but he is only tiny and can't sit up yet."

Mrs. Gabriel tickled her grandson under the chin and was rewarded with a toothless baby grin. She nodded towards the bluebells the child was clutching.

"Those are pretty" she smiled "who are those for?"

"These are for my Granny's picture – she has died and gone to heaven you know and Auntie Rosa put primroses there, but I know that my Granny likes bluebells."

This reminded her of her loss and the tears welled up again.

"What a nice idea" replied the old lady quickly, anxious to stem the tide. She was perfectly well aware of the passing of Alice as the two old ladies had grown to know each other well over the past forty years. She was a sad loss.

"You know," she went on, "the bluebells and the new babies are a sign that life does go on and the old always have to make way for the new my dear."

"Granddad said that she was always in too much of a hurry and that he would catch her up!"

Mrs. Gabriel stifled a grin and slipped the brake on the pram as baby Peter started to grizzle. She jiggled it up and down again and he stopped.

"I think my Granddad has got a television too" Joan confided, "though I haven't seen it yet, he does have a big pole with an H on in his garden though."

"How wonderful dear," she replied, slightly amused that a man who would not go on the telephone had got a television already. "You take care of your Granddad," she smiled as she started to move away, "he is a good man and the salt of the earth?"

"Yes I will," Joan replied. She couldn't possibly imagine a world without her Granddad in it – that was much too huge to think about.

Mrs. Gabriel straightened the baby in his pram.

"Well, goodbye for now my dear," she said as she pointed it in the direction of the Manor, "I had better get this child back to my son and daughter-in-law."

She watched the old lady walk slowly off down the drive and then go through the gate into the vegetable garden and out of sight and then an almighty gust of wind made her realise that she had better get on back or incur the wrath of her mother.

She ran across the field back to the cottage, all the time wondering what 'salt of the earth' meant and, above all, to make sure that Granddad was still there.

He was sitting in the old familiar chair by the fireplace with his family around him.

"I met Mrs. Gabriel and baby Peter" she announced.

"Ah yes," said Charles "she's been a good soul – I bet Kate is up there now keeping an eye on her old man for her!"

"Dad!" cried Rosa, Doris and Lily together. He was incorrigible.

Charles went to the sideboard and poured out a sherry for them all and Rosa gave the children some orange juice. He raised his glass towards the picture.

"To Kate!" he muttered, "bless her heart wherever she is."

"To Mum" said everyone else together.

Joan was still vaguely looking for the television when Charles did something really magical and totally unexpected – something that only somebody who was 'the salt of the earth' would think of when he had all five of his grandchildren present.

None of the children had noticed a big box in the corner of the room covered in a flowery cloth until now. He whisked it off like a magician and switched a knob on the front. Then he went round and pulled all the curtains tight shut, just as if it was the black out again..

"Thank goodness you have put us out of our misery at last Dad," said Stan

"We are going to watch the Boat Race" announced Charles.

Joan knew exactly what the Boat Race was. Her parents listened to it on the wireless every year and dad always said Oxford would win while mum supported Cambridge. To actually see it was like a miracle.

The television had a small window in the front and, after it had warmed up, a picture appeared just like at the cinema but in your own front room. It was no surprise to the adults because they clearly knew what was coming but it was certainly a wonder to the four older children.

They all cheered and clapped when a very grainy black and white picture of the River Thames appeared and the two boats lined up ready for their race. Joan, Roger, Michael and Margaret just stared open mouthed at this piece of magic before their eyes. Richard just slept through it.

It was something very remarkable that took young minds off the recent sad events and filled the adults with awe as they silently gazed at the picture in the corner of the room and listened to the commentary.

"I've never known them be so quiet," whispered Doris.

The weather was appalling though and Lily felt quite sorry for the chaps out there on the water. Charles leaned over and turned the volume up and they all listened carefully. Suddenly Lily and Stan were taking sides again.

"Oxford is going to win" said Stan.

"No" replied Lily just to be opposite, "Cambridge."

The sadness of what had happened just a couple of months ago was temporarily forgotten as everyone vied with everyone else to cheer on their favourite crew as they battled against the elements.

Then, just as they reached a bend in the River at Fulham, a fierce cross wind caught Oxford sideways and the boat started to fill up with water. The picture was so small and shaky that it was hard to make out what was happening until, suddenly, the boat disappeared from underneath them!

"Oh my God" cried Rosa, "they've sunk!"

For a few seconds there was just a row of heads, one behind the other sticking out of the water, until suddenly they realised their predicament and swam for it. It was a measure of the power of the television that all those in the room were more fascinated in the picture in front of them than they were concerned about the fate of the Oxford crew!

"Well, I think Cambridge have won this year," laughed Lily.

"There," said Doris as she handed round more cake, "not only can you tell your friends that you have seen a television but you can tell them that you actually saw Oxford sink – won't that be something to talk about in the future?"

"We'll have a television one day," said Stan, "but we will have to save up for it."

"We'll see about that" replied Lily, "it will take a lot of saving for."

Joan pulled her chair up at the side of Granddad's and watched the magic box until the outside broadcast from a boat on the River Thames finished. Not before, however, that it was announced that the race would be rowed again in two days time. Then he leaned over and switched it off.

"All gone for now," he said, "it's only fair that they have the race again – poor old Oxford."

The picture disappeared and was replaced for a short while by a shiny dot and then it was gone. Auntie Rosa put the flowery cloth back over it and an ornament on the top and so it had temporarily disappeared from view, much to Joan and Roger's disappointment.

"I would have liked Kate to have seen it" said Charles.

"Truth be known" whispered Rosa to Lily, "Mum wouldn't have been interested – she didn't like new fangled things – hadn't really got used to the wireless!"

Charles ignored the comment.

"We shall have to get saving Doris," said Harry, "We'll have one soon."

Doris liked the wireless but she realised that life was moving on and eventually everyone would have a television in the corner of their room – and it was exciting to see the Boat Race.

It occurred to Lily that, unusually, Charles had beaten her father to the modern gadgets. Henry had always been proud that he was the only one in the family with a gramophone, but he hadn't progressed to a flush toilet yet – never mind a television.

"And he was the one that thought a gardener's son was not good enough!" she silently thought.

All too soon it was time to go home. It was just as well that the violent March storm that had ended the Boat Race had blown itself out and only a few puddles remained as a consequence.

Charles did not change the habits already started by Alice though. He had a packet of pear drops ready for everyone and waved to his family until they were out of sight. Only when they were all finally gone did he turn round and go back indoors where Rosa was waiting for him gallantly trying to fill the void left by her mother. She never could.

Then he caught sight of Roger's aeroplane picture which he had left behind and he propped it up at the side of Joan's rainbow with a satisfied nod.

Alice would always be missed by everyone but, as the pictures proved, things *do* work out in the end – especially if you have pictures painted for you by grandchildren that love you very much – Hitler and his 'nasties', as his eldest grandchild called them, never had anything like that.

Epilogue

Summer 1951 – No.2 Timber Site

Britain was picking itself up from the war and, as if to prove it, the Festival of Britain was built on the huge area that had been bombed on London's South Bank. There was bomb damage all around but this exhibition was defiantly telling the world that we had come through and that an exciting new era was beginning. The Britain that Alice, Charles, Grace and Henry had been born into had gone forever, and Stan and Lily were going to have to adjust to fiction becoming fact.

All the top classes of the Junior School were taken on the train to see the wonders of the Dome of Discovery and the big cigar shaped Skylon, although most of them were too young to appreciate most of it.

The children came back with armfuls of leaflets and with stories about what they had seen.

"We saw lots of televisions all in rows", said Joan, "and there were polar bears, and Alice in Wonderland going through the Looking Glass, and we had rock with the letters going through it, and there was a cinema where you wore red and green glasses and it was like you were in the picture." She paused for breath,

"Oh, and Joyce Brock was sick all over the pavement."

Stan studied the leaflets – it was like looking into the future and yet it was just six years since the war ended – as long it had lasted.

There was even talk of man eventually going into space which seemed very hard to believe for someone who could remember bringing back the bodies from the crashed R101 all those years ago – and yet he was not yet forty. He wondered what his grandfather, the old 'turnip top' John Ratcliff would make of it all.

“..and there were lots of places to get all different coloured ice creams...” Joan was still chattering away regardless of whether anyone was listening or not.

Meanwhile Lily looked at the leaflets showing gadgets that she never dreamed of – food mixers, toasters and tables made out of stuff called Formica. There were even pictures of refrigerators to keep food cold. She thought of Alice and her ‘well’ in the garden – she never did like gadgets. Then she thought of her mother still living down the bottom of the lane with no proper plumbing and wondered if her father would ever be likely to get a house with a bath before Grace got too old to use one!

Just at the start of the school holidays a letter from the Council was delivered to No.2 Timber Site. After six years of living in the train carriage, Lily was to get her own bathroom at last. Along with Coxy and his family, they were to be re-housed. She had mixed feelings about the prospect – however, it had to be done. She knew that they could not live here forever, but the years since the end of the war had been the happiest of her life – that is, until the passing of Alice. In one way the timing was ‘divine providence’ though, because it was another thing to help take their minds from their loss and look once again to the future.

Joan wasn’t too sure about leaving her train carriage home at all and as, bit by bit, the furniture started to disappear and then her toys, her fears were confirmed. It smacked of being evacuated again. No matter how many times Lily tried to tell her that it wasn’t ‘proper’ evacuation anyway, it was to her, and she didn’t want to go back to sleeping in a tiny alcove and wearing gas masks ever again. Neither did she want to go in that nasty cot in the Infirmary which she could still vaguely remember. But, as always, she could be bribed!

One day, as the two older children were indoors listening to ‘Dick Barton – Special Agent’ on the wireless and Richard had been fed and put in his cot Stan arrived home from work carrying a tiny little bundle clinging to his shoulder.

"Oh look what your father has brought home" cried Lily as he lifted the small fluffy ball from beneath his collar and held it in the palm of his hand.

Dick Barton was forgotten as both children ran up to their Dad. He had kept his promise. Joan held out both her hands and took the tiny black and white kitten from him as Michael looked on.

"We must get him some milk – we need a saucer Mum."

"No good getting a saucer," laughed Stan, "the poor little devil will swim in it."

"Is it a boy or a girl?" queried Joan.

"It is a little boy" replied Stan. "What are you going to call him?"

"Peter" was the immediate reply.

"That's a funny name for a cat," said Lily as she emerged from the kitchen with the lid of a paste pot and poured the tiniest amount of milk in it.

"It is after Mrs. Gabriel's baby grandson Peter – I promised her that if I had a new kitten I would call him Peter and also after the boy in my class."

"What if it had been a little girl kitten?" said Stan.

"Still Peter." She put him down on the floor and watched as he licked up the milk in the paste pot lid. Michael went back to playing with his cars. His sister's daft ideas were all beyond him and he was still unaware of the impending upheaval in his life. Little did he know it but he would soon have the benefit of proper friends to play with instead of imaginary ones and it was not before time. There had been no-one else other than his sister and her friends and their games nearly always ended in arguments!

At least three out of the five members of the family were very nostalgic on the last evening in the train carriage and Joan found it hard not to cry especially when she realised that they would have to leave her swing behind and she would not have the meadows to play in any more. Eventually though, peace reigned once she was assured that Peter the cat would not be left behind!

"A door opens as another shuts".

"Listen to that," said Stan when he and Lily were finishing off their final packing.

"I can't hear anything," she replied, just grateful that her eldest had stopped complaining about moving.

"Exactly," he smiled, "the silence of three children sleeping their last sleep at No.2 Timber Site – it's the end of an era Lil'."

He glanced across at the Daily Mirror with Winston's face on the front as usual, and decided to paraphrase one of his well known speeches of the war. In the fashion of Charles, he put a pencil in his mouth and raised his cup of tea in the air.

"It is not the end" he mimicked, "but it can be looked upon as the end of the beginning."

"The beginning of the rest of our lives," said Lily.

They both knew that once they had emptied the train carriage of all their final bits of furniture and mementos it would be just a shell that would be taken away and broken up.

The 'iron things' that had been everything to the children from camping sites and ships in full sail to climbing frames, magic caves and even, for Michael, a garage, would be removed and the place levelled. It had served its purpose well though and soon all the trees and blackberry bushes would be cut down and the area would be returned to just what it was originally intended to be – nothing more than a reservoir surrounded by the hills with the flowers constantly 'mowed' by the sheep. The coltsfoot and primroses would disappear in an instant and Nos. 1 and 2 Timber Site would be no more. It was impossible not to be a bit sad as Stan went outside to the old air raid shelter and came back with the spade to dig the Peace rose up – that was going with them.

It was ten years since he had been Duty NCO in Malta. It was only by 'divine providence' that he had lived to see his daughter. As for his sons – they, like him, owed their very existence to the vagaries of the duty rota at RAF Luqa which put him on nights when his billet had a direct hit. Future generations had a lot to thank that duty rota for!

The austere forties had given way to the hopeful fifties. Rationing had almost ended although sweets would need coupons for some while – much to Joan's disgust. People were still eating bread and dripping and there were plenty of bombed out buildings to be seen. But the sight of the Festival of Britain on the South Bank was enough to reassure everybody that a whole new and promising future lay ahead.

Only a couple of hundred yards from the train carriage, in a place called Field Common, there were people living in little more than shacks or caravans and slightly further away the last of the big silver barrage balloons hung in the air. They were among the last remnants of an era gone.

Exactly one year after Alice died, in February 1952, King George VI sadly passed away. Everyone was genuinely upset but sales of televisions rocketed as people realised that they would be able to watch a Royal funeral for the first time in history.

Exactly one year after that there would be a Coronation and even Stan could not fight off the need to join the twentieth century any longer. Not when there was the possibility of seeing the 'once in a lifetime' spectacle of the crowning of the young Queen Elizabeth at her Coronation.

Even the loss of Joan's swing paled into insignificance at the thought of having the box in the corner! In any case, she could go to the swings in the park now and she had all her friends from school to go with. Also they had a proper bath at last instead of a tin tub.

As it was, despite being born in the war, she had been fortunate enough to spend most of her childhood in two very special places. Somehow the little bit of 'Camelot' that was Coxhill escaped any real damage from doodlebugs or bombs and the gardens, both at the cottage and at the Manor, bloomed under Charles' tender loving care.

Similarly, with the minor exception of the gun in the blackberry bushes, No's 1 and 2 Timber Site remained a safe haven where the cuckoo was always heard in the spring and tadpoles swam in the stream where the children played poo-sticks. Despite the rationing and doing without many things, they contented themselves with looking for four leaf clovers or sliding on tin trays down the reservoir hills, happy with their lot, wanting nothing and believing implicitly in Father Christmas and God in his heaven.

They were two of 'nature's half-acres' in the middle of the unbelievable carnage done by the Germans who so very nearly, invaded our country such a short time ago. It would be another generation, maybe two, before people would realise how very, very close we came to being under the jackboot. One thing was certain though – everyone had been through some very extraordinary times and from now on – ordinary would do – though with planes going faster than sound and talk of space ships, Stan had a shrewd suspicion that things would not stay ordinary for very long. There was, however, something that he did know for an absolute certainty – no matter what lay in store he and Lily would be together forever and, as his father once said "the next fifty years would be a cakewalk!"

Moreover, there were three children who were very, very glad that he was not left in a foreign field!

~ END ~